Thank you to all who have contributed to this book:
Ulrika Jonsson
Mark Lamarr
Matt Lucas

Thank you also to:
Alan Marke and Lisa Thomas at Channel X.
Charlie Higson, Mark Mylod and David G. Croft.
Antony Genn for producing the CD.
Andy Blackburn for many questions.
Lisa Matthews and Roma Koiser for our lovely suits.
Chiggy and Melanie at PBJ Management.
Everybody at BBC Books.

This book is published to accompany the BBC television series
entitled *Shooting Stars*.

Executive Producer Jon Plowman
Producer Alan Marke
Director Mark Mylod

Published by BBC Books,
an imprint of BBC Worldwide Publishing.
BBC Worldwide Limited, Woodlands,
80 Wood Lane, London W12 0TT.

First published 1996
Reprinted 1996
© Vic Reeves and Bob Mortimer 1996
The moral right of the authors has been asserted

ISBN 0 563 38784 X

Designed by Design/Section
Cartoons by Simon Donald
Photographs by Stuart Wood
Illustrations on pages 34 - 35 and 110 - 117 by Vic Reeves

Set in News Gothic and Helvetica Compressed
Printed and bound in Belgium by Proost NV
Colour separations by Radstock Reproductions Ltd, Midsomer Norton
Cover printed by Proost NV

Shooting Stars

Welcome, whoever you are ...

1   You may have been awarded this book by the factory where you have toiled for the past forty years, as a gift in recognition of your retirement.

2   You may have found it in a dusty attic seventy years after publication, in which case you are probably employed by the salt people polishing their giant saltcellars in preparation for the great condiment war against the vinegar men. (p.s. the vinegar men win 2–1.)

3   You may have been given it by the Queen instead of an OBE that she has just run out of.

4   It may have rained down on you, along with other comedy publications, in a bizarre fluke rainstorm from the Sahara Desert.

5   Or you may have bought it, believing it to be a kind of readable herring.

Whichever of the above it is, we hope you enjoy reading the book and playing the game.

Remember: beer on wine feel fine; wine on beer feel queer.

Meet **Mark**

Day One, February 3rd 1959. Buddy Holly dies. Seconds later I'm found wrapped in a pair of drainpipe trousers on the steps of Bermondsey Police Station with half a sixpence clutched in my hand. My parents never come forward but rumours of Tommy Steele's involvement abound.
My first year is spent sleeping rough under tarpaulins, and these happy-go-lucky days usually find me playing the spoons in London's seamy Soho.

Day 438. Disaster strikes. One of my spoons breaks. I realize that playing the spoons is not a viable musical career when my usual crowd-stopper, 'Hound Dog', is met with silence. I decide that the only way to raise money for another spoon is to sell my soul to Satan. So, off I trek to the crossroads for my date with the Devil. As luck would have it, Nicodemus and his hoary demons of the nether world are held up at a party at Henry Kelly's house and I have a chance to read the paper. Here I discover that Eddie Cochran has been tragically killed in a tragic car accident. It is an omen

and I see the light. Either that or I see the light and it is an omen. Whatever, not only do I find God, I also find an easier way to make a living: theft.

For the next year my passport profession is listed as pickpocket. Round the gaily lit streets of London's West End, my eager hands fondle the lining of many a gentleman's suit and respectable lady's undergarments in search of all that is green or shiny. I can sell a pocket watch for two and six (eight) and with the extra money I earn spinning gold from straw for distressed princesses, I can make ten bob or a pony a week (which in 1961 was sod all).

My luck changes the day I meet the Entwistles, my foster parents. Dave Entwistle, a handsome, hairy, horn-rimmed, hallway of a man and his wife Alice, an attractive, agile Alsatian, treat me like the half-man half-dog they never had. Everyday is like a holiday with Dave and Alice (mainly because we live in a caravan and travel the country due to Dave's peg-selling business). I try to treat the Entwistles like my real parents, telling them I hate them and asking 'Why?' whenever they tell me to do anything. If I'd gone to school I'm sure these would have been the happiest days of my life. As it is, I am never really comfortable with

their odd method of toilet training and Dave's obsession with fences. I've never known a man to hate boundaries so badly. No sooner do we park in a field than Dave is hacking away at the nearest post and Alice is running around scaring livestock and defecating. We build lovely fires and eat whatever pheasants and chickens Alice manages to carry back in her mouth, and, despite her primitive recipes (usually consisting of soaking partly chewed meat in saliva), the food always tasted like raw meat dragged through mud. Once a week the locals in every town drive out to our caravan and give a great welcoming cheer before playing a game called 'Let's slap the Gypos about'. It is nice to have people to play with for a change but sometimes the playing is a bit rough and I pray to the Lord God, baby Jesus, for it to stop.

October 12th 1971. Gene Vincent dies. It is a bad day, especially for Gene Vincent. On the other hand I doubt if he would have been happy in my place, setting thrush traps at dawn in the Malvern Hills while my foster mum sits around licking her arse and my foster dad whittles. In my dreams I am rescued by a gang of Christian bikers and whisked off to Cliff Richard's secret bunker for wayward boys but it is never to be. Alas, that very day I am taken away, not by the Huguenots on Harleys but by a fearsome gang known only as the 'Authorities'. This is my first ever night spent in a building. I am twelve years old but I know deep down that I won't always be.

My first years in prison are mostly wasted fetching sticks for the other inmates and occasionally begging or playing dead. First of all I found it degrading when they made me walk on my hind legs but after a few months I quite enjoyed it and joined in their silly game. My only regret is that I've never shaken the habit since.

By the time I am eighteen (Elvis dies), I have learned a few rudimentary words and in fact become quite good at what I think is called 'speaking'. I start selling snouts on the inside, keeping my nose clean, doing me porridge, stealing pineapple chunks and staying away from that two-faced scrote, Ives.

Upon my release I am all set to go into business. On my return to London, heavily laden with nylons, bananas and ration books, I am shocked to discover rock 'n' roll is dead and punk rockers, who laugh at my hair, are the new rulers of the street. I decide I will have the last laugh but of course I am wrong.

I stay in during the eighties, living on bananas, ration books and nylons, watching television in the hope that Chas and Dave or Mike Reid might be on and shaking with fear everytime Jerry Lee Lewis has an operation. We can't afford to lose another one, I can't stand any more bad luck. It is during Jerry's last illness that Mr Reeves and Mr Mortimer approach me to be on a light-hearted comedy quiz show (or so they tell me). The rest of this sad story you can witness with your own eyes.

Meet # Ulrika

Dear Ulrika,

We hope you are well and not recieving too much hassle from the immigration people

We are currently writing the 'Shooting Stars' book and wondered if you would write a few kind words for inclusion in said book.

If you were to use the following wording; "I consider Mr Reeves and Mr Mortimer to be the most intelligent, attractive, erotic and sporty presenters on tv"

We in return <u>promise</u> + <u>quarentee</u> to print an attractive photograph of you to accompany your words.

Yours Sincerely.

Vic & Bob.

RED LION PUB AND GRILL
East End of London

To whom it may concern
I consider Mr Reeves and Mr Mortimer to be
the most intelligent, attractive, erotic
and sporty presenters on tv.

Signed

X

Ulrika Jonsson

How to **leg rub**

Locate and approach a brassy tart. For maximum enticement an approach from behind or the side is to be preferred.

Use your leading foot to test the ground for grip and static which might cause pubic tingling during the rub.

Third stage rubbing is mistakenly commenced. The body is lowered, the cravat is allowed to swing freely in the breeze and the facial expression is that of a wanton monkey trying to expel a batch of underipe mangoes.

Far from being enticed the victim is offended and sickened.

Commence first stage rubbing from an almost upright position. The strokes must be FAST, your face FOCUSED and your victim must not be FRIGHTENED.

Second stage rubbing is well underway. The knees are bent and both hands are moving in unison. It is very erotic. However, this victim is showing signs of repulsion which should alert the rubber to bail out, but it's too late.

Her natural reaction is to strike out and repel the beast.

The rub is over, the tart remains unenticed and the beast is dormant.

Meet George Dawes

'Hallo Mama. I George Dawes. I cool dude. I ain't no motherlover.'

These words, uttered at birth by the baby himself, perhaps tell us all we need to know about this eponymous entity. Rarely has one individual had quite so much effect and influence on the culture of his time …

Meet George Bubba Dawes …

Three men – Reeves, Mortimer and Lamarr – brought gifts and knelt at the side of the manger: gold, frankincense and a *Pingu*.

As George rode alone on the back of a donkey, he stopped in each and every town he passed through and by tapping percussive rhythms on the wounds of the sick, he quickly gained a loyal following.

One day, whilst resting with his disciples, George was distracted by a quarrelling couple.

'My wife has stolen my oxen,' said the man.

'I believe they are rightfully mine,' said the woman.

'What are the laws, George Dawes?' asked the couple.

George deliberated before solving the problem.

Years later, in medieval England, George was approached by an aspiring playwright called William Shakespeare who was depressed after his first play had been rejected by the RSC.

'What are the flaws, George Dawes?' asked William Shakespeare.

George deliberated before solving the problem.

It was dynamic leadership qualities such as these that led to George's involvement, once more, with the errant comic twosome, Reeves and Mortimer. …Oh yeah, and Mark Lamarr. …Oh yeah, and something called Ulrikakaka Jonsson.

And now, George resides in judgement over the hilarious, zany, post-modern, surreal comedy quiz *Shooting Stars*.

Fear for the children.

50

things to do with

your

1 Cross them to bring good fortune to your family, and in times of national crisis, the whole country.

2 Stick them in a dripping dyke to save Holland from flooding.

3 Run through the hair of a loved one to create a feeling of wellbeing and express affection.

4 Use as a shoe horn.

5 Beat out an irritating rhythm on your desk to annoy workmates.

6 Cover in orange juice and stick your fingers in the freezer. Hey presto, a lollipop on a finger.

7 Point at an accident in the high street.

8 Crush a wasp or a fly or an ant. (Not a spider as it brings bad luck, see.)

9 Test temperature of porridge (if you are a bear).

10 Offer to a friend to smell after you have fingered a trout.

11 Put in end of a ketchup bottle to seal in the contents as you shake it to loosen the tomato goodness from the walls of the bottle.

12 Chop ends off and claim invalidity benefit.

13 Point out nude on continental beach.

14 Flick dog dirt out of your horse's mane.

15 Flick through *Grattons* catalogue to locate the lingerie section.

fingers

16   Put deep into throat to trigger spew valve.

17   Smear the words 'I will kill again' on to the wall following your latest murder.

18   Push your piles back into position.

19   Wipe away a tear whilst viewing hubby's autopsy.

20   Indicate location of gas pipe.

21   Scrape away at granite wall when incarcerated in a high-security prison.

22   Brush away stray dog hair from painting of salad.

23   Lick and point in the air to give impression you are a scientist investigating wind directions.

24   Put inside a glove puppet to entertain a toddler or senile relation.

25   Plunge into a saucepan, then announce to the cook 'Oh, what a rich sauce'.

26   Apply pressure to a spot or recent cut to stem the blood flow.

27   Hook guest's camel coat out of swimming pool.

28   Push your spectacles back on to nose to give impression of great knowledge and wisdom.

29   Count severance pay prior to suicide.

30   Smear faeces or blood on to public-toilet wall prior to writing time and date of said smearing.

31 Push banana into deep space.

32 Push dog's erection into its cover.

33 Ram into pigeon's throat to recover your lost tasty peanuts.

34 Cover eyes of dolphin when riding through the South Seas.

35 Lock toilet doors to keep out persistent homosexuals.

36 Cover a complete stranger's eyes from behind and say 'Guess who', before apologizing for your error.

37 Twang a lady's long strap as a kind of playful first move.

38 Twang a boy's posing pouch etc., etc.

39 If blind, use to feel your way around a town centre.

40 Revolve to the side of your head to indicate a member of the party has lost their marbles.

41 Plunge into a Battenburg cake, thus ruining its charm, then offer to buy it at half price.

42 Take photo of one and use to head a newspaper column entitled 'The Fickled Finger of Filth'.

43 Place over end of a hose-pipe to achieve longer spray when watering distant marigolds.

44 Scratch eczema.

45 Move peanuts away from eyes when sleeping in the grounds of a KP factory.

46 Perform an initial test on a cat flap.

47 Lift up fringe to see road signs whilst driving.

48 Put in ears whilst listening to Meatloaf.

49 Point out a busybody to a gossip columnist.

50 And finally, of course, apply false eyelashes to a duck.

Isn't she

lovely?

Interview with Mark Lamarr

Bob: Welcome to *London in the Afternoon* with Bob Mortimer and Vic Reeves.

Bob: Have you got any tattoos?

Mark: Yes.

Bob: What's it of?

Mark: Yogi Bear.

Vic: Why did you have Yogi Bear, is he your favourite cartoon character? Does it cause a stir when you strip in front of a gentleman or a lady?

Mark: Yes.

Vic: What do they say?

Mark: 'Oh you've got a tattoo!'

Vic: Don't they say 'Yabadabadoo'?

Vic: Have you ever had a perm?

Mark: No.

Vic: That was very quick off the mark, I think you might have done.

Mark: You think I've got one underneath this?

Vic: Well, I wouldn't like to say. There might be a little tight perm under there.

Bob: The hair. When did that all start?

Mark: When I was about three or four months.

Bob: The style I mean.

Mark: When I was about seventeen.

Vic: Was it a conscious decision?

Mark: I tried to do it when I was sixteen but it didn't work.

Vic: Your perm hadn't grown out then.

Bob: Was it copied off anybody. Is it meant to look like somebody, say George Strummer or Alfie Bass or what?

Mark:	No.
Bob:	Do you ever vary the length of your sideboards?
Mark:	Yes, frequently.
Bob:	And do you find there's an ideal length that you can never get back to.
Mark:	No.
Bob:	Have you ever used anything on your hair in an emergency?
Mark:	No.
Bob:	Who was your favourite guest on *Shooting Stars*?
Mark:	John Peel.
Bob:	Is that because you have an in-built affection for the man?
Mark:	I have no affection for him whatsoever, but it was the pram.
Vic:	You've got a lot of records, haven't you – how many?
Mark:	Ten thousand.
Vic:	Get out! Ten thousand!
Bob:	Have you listened to them all?
Mark:	Yes.
Bob:	Do you ever buy one and think it's rubbish?
Mark:	Yes.
Vic:	When it comes to the crunch between the Homepride Flour men and the Tetley Tea folk, who's going to win the final battle.
Mark:	Tetley Tea folk, definitely.
Vic:	Really. Why? Are they harder?
Mark:	Well, the Homepride Flour men dress in suits and think they're the Krays, but they're not, they're just giving it some.
Vic:	They're just big, dumb Yorkshiremen with big hats.
Mark:	I've heard that the Tetley Tea folk are really into martial arts.
Bob:	You might like to dwell on the fact that you can actually make a bomb out of flour.
Vic:	Can't make a bomb out of tea.
Bob:	You can if you're selling it.
Vic:	What's your favourite burger?
Mark:	Maybe a turkey burger.
Vic:	Don't you ever go for beef?
Mark:	I like beef, yeah.
Vic:	Are you worried about the current scare?
Mark:	No.
Vic:	What about tuberculosis?
Mark:	Slightly.
Bob:	We'll see if we've got some leaflets that can help on that.
Mark:	Tell me when I can go home.
Bob:	Thank you very much Mark.

Guests

John Craven
John Craven hasn't changed a lot since his days as the original lead singer in Genesis. His mind is strong and physically he seems quite well, although he does camp on about Beatrix Potter and he's always going round telling people that he's a 'fair dinkum cobber' for an Aussie! Hmmm. John arrived in a bit of a state having dropped two Es and a tab of acid the previous evening.

John Peel
Bumbling John Peel ambles around the sleepy village where he lives, bumping into trees and lampposts and picking flowers, which he catalogues before stuffing them into his Weetabix cupboard. Freud called the body 'the mansion' of the soul; John Peel's soul dwells in a kind of run-down tin shack with an exotic interior decorated with rich tapestries and ceramics vases.

Darcus Howe
Darcus arrived astride a giant, motorized winkle. He descended from its haunches wearing a revolving chicken-and-mushroom-pie hat and propelled himself on to the studio floor in his winking macadamia-nut love machine.

Noddy Holder
Loveable, gullible, fish-faced Noddy runs a horsefly sanctuary where he cares for sick and elderly horseflies. At several times during the show, recording had to be stopped due to a bubbling sound coming from the brewer's yeast in his trouser pockets. After the show, Noddy insisted on going for a curry.

Sara Cox

'Eee by gum she's reet gradely,' cry the folk of Ilkley Moor bah t'at as she strides down the high street displaying her well-rounded, beautifully-formed Yorkshire puddings. Yes, she really does love her 'Udders feeled'!

Carol Vorderman

High-ranking soap-powder scrutineer, white-coated scientific-type lass, Carol, when not doing sums and counting and that, loves to use those big baby-blue eyes to entice Greek yoghurt out of its pots. We were surprised to find out that Carol was over seven foot tall and completely bald. She smoked like a chimney throughout the recording, changing to a pipe later on.

Eric Bristow

Gorgeous, seven-foot Eric is the thinking woman's favourite piece of crumpet. He freely admits to having bonked his way to the top and puts his prowess down to his diet of fried eggs, scrag end and semolina.

Jarvis Cocker

Jarvis arrived in a glass bottle usually reserved for stick insects and was immediately deposited in the bowels of the Natural History Unit. Pouting, rubber-hipped, thin-lipped, flat-chested Jarvis recently held a wife-swapping party on his estate; sadly Jarvis had no takers as he is married to a monkey.

Chris Evans

Multi-millionaire Chris is, in real life, startlingly beautiful, like a young porcelain cat. His translucent skin reveals the delicate blue veins beneath and his titian hair is so fine and flyaway that bits of it do, indeed, fly away, to the sea where all titian hairs go. Here they reclaim their rightful place, swimming amid rocks and coral, waiting to once again rule the earth.

Monday

Arrive at office prompt. A businessman rings with an exciting offer which we decline. Ten minutes later, another businessman rings with a similar offer which we accept. We then interview a woman for a job, to no avail. Soon after, Jools Holland, the flash pianist, enters the office bearing yet another grudge against local developers. To us, his remarks seem futile but he is granted a pardon as he leaves. For two hours we pursue a wasp to no avail. At 3.30 pm an ape enters the building. We go home. It's been a busy day.

Tuesday

Bob arrives at office prompt, claiming to be an expert picture framer. Having no evidence to back this up, he quickly drops his claim and a pardon is granted. Vic turns up prompt dressed as Barry Crier. He explains that he has a champagne cork trapped up his jacksy and it's the only thing that seems to help. Well, he will lead the high life! Midday, Bob searches through his catalogue for a new type of toupee, to no avail. Vic spots lager lout through binoculars, turns to Bob for verification only to discover he left the office three hours ago.

Wednesday

Arrive at office prompt. Still reeling from excitement of previous night. Vic notices that Bob has been on fire for the previous two hours. He asks Bob how the fire started. Bob can't remember and so the matter passes. Ho hum. Spend three

hours working on a possible solution to drought to no avail. Begin work on film script in which a small banjo-playing hillbilly is found living in a man's throat. Working title is 'The Throatbilly'. 4.00 pm, suddenly and unexpectedly Vic rises out of his seat claiming to be blind. Bob is unconcerned and leaves the office to cut up some bits of carpet to go in his van. Meet up 9.00 pm, Chelsea Harbour, to have a look at a billboard with a picture of a beef Wellington on it. 3.00 am realize it is not a beef Wellington but a bottle of lucozade. Walk home disgusted with ourselves for having wasted an entire evening.

Thursday

Didn't make it home last night and so awaken at 12.30 pm in school playground and run to the office playing catch kissy. Bob is Byron. Vic is Jennifer Rush. Arrive at office to find it engulfed in flames. Ask attending fire chief how the fire started.

He can't remember so the matter passes. 3.00 pm, disaster strikes! An intense fireball spews forth from Vic's boiled egg and lands in Bob's flammable slacks. Vic takes his bag of eggs back to the shop for refund only to find it is engulfed in flames. When Vic suggests to attending fire officer that the cause of fire may be flammable eggs he is frogmarched for approximately one hour by a couch potato who looks like Ron from *Brookside*.

One military hour later, Robert Wagner from *Hart to Hart* telephones. Good news, he is holding an egg buffet at his Canary Wharf apartment and Vic and Bob are invited

Canary Wharf, 8.30 pm. Vic's revolver unexpectedly goes off, shooting him in the foot. Feels it inappropriate to attend Robert's rented accommodation with injured foot so goes to pictures instead and sees film. Can't remember what. Something to do with a lighthouse.

Friday
Best day of the week as we both bring packed lunches. Vic's lunchbox contains: one part roasted quail, eight sultanas, a mini bite, a selection of louse brains, apple and fish-lung salad, cow's-arse fudge.
Bob's contains: apple, crisps, Mars bar, chicken sandwich.

Vic successfully persuades Bob to swap lunches. Bob wishes he'd never been born, to no avail. Rest of day taken up with interviews with press and meetings with Crystal Palace F.C. officials concerning our forthcoming TV series. Four military hours later Bob joins T.A. Vic drives scooter through Harrods' window in attempted smash-and-grab. Gets away with preserve-filled hamper.

Meet up 8.00 pm, at what at first sight appears to be set of working gallows, but later transpires to be a pub sign. Disgusted with ourselves for wasting yet more military hours, we walk home.

Saturday

Hooray! The clocks go back. Celebrations over, we proceed to local shopping precinct to buy the week's provisions. Spend two hours choosing apple to hollow out and use as candle holder. Bob unexpectedly decides he is Colin Cowdry and harasses people to ask him for his autograph. Meanwhile Vic wanders aroud W.H. Smiths asking customers whether they were cavaliers or roundheads.

4.00pm, both ejected from precinct for urinating over shoe display outside Dolcis.

5.00 pm, football results. We tick off town names in our atlas as they are mentioned. Couldn't find Norwich. Hope they are playing next week so we can try again.

8.30 pm, meet up outside Radio Rentals and spend nice night watching telly. Poured down with rain. Programmes end 12.40 am. Walk home drenched, but happy.

Sunday

Bob's lung collapses but re-inflates in seconds. Vic has lunch at Lassiters. Bob sees cobra in pantry. Vic fails to spot sniper dressed as a clown on hot-dog stand outside flat. Bob hits cobra with tabasco bottle. Sniper's bullet narrowly misses Vic's face. Cobra leaves dwelling. Celebrate by cooking omelette. House engulfed in flames.

It is the only country that sounds like 'sweeten' said with a cold.

Sweden's group Abba is named after the first letters of its members' names: Alan, Brenda, Bill and Aunty Mary.

Sweden's flag features a Ryvita in conversation with a monkey nut.

It is legal to take your clothes off in Sweden.

No one has ever tasted, or even heard of, curry in Sweden.

Saab is named after the four inventors: Stuart, Alan, Aunty Mary and Bill.

Things about Sweden

Sweden is famous for its lighthouses, the tallest of which is 180 miles high. If you drop a penny off the top, it would look like it was sleeping peacefully on top of a Chevy.

Smorgasbord, the Swedish national dish, is named after its inventors: Stuart, Moira, Old Bill, Ron, Gripper, Aunty Mary, Sandra, Brenda, Old Dick, Randy Sue and Derek Nimmo.

The suicide rate is so high that tall buildings are banned.

Sweden is named after its inventors: Stuart, Wanky Don, Ed the Duck, Dirty Bill, The Edge and Normski.

20	20	20	20	20
19	19	19	19	19
18	18	18	18	18
17	17	17	17	17
16	16	16	16	16
15	15	15	15	15
14	14	14	14	14
13	13	13	13	13
12	12	12	12	12
11	11	11	11	11
10	10	10	10	10
9	9	9	9	9
8	8	8	8	8
7	7	7	7	7
6	6	6	6	6
5	5	5	5	5
4	4	4	4	4
3	3	3	3	3
2	2	2	2	2
1	1	1	1	1

Born Eva Ulrika Jonsson in 1967 on a council estate outside Stockholm.

Holds a 130 w.p.m. shorthand certificate.

Mother was Gun, father Bo.

Cadbury's 'Rear of the Year' 1992.

Moved to England at the age of twelve.

Notorious for making hoax phone calls.

Spends her evenings drinking whisky and memorizing weather statistics.

Has only ever had seven pairs of Marks and Spencer knickers, which she continually repairs.

Things about Ulrika

Always greets people with the expression, 'It's lovely to meet you, down amongst the lingon berries.'

Favourite car is a Saab.

Favourite furniture store is IKEA.

Only drinks milk with her dinner.

Lost her hair in a prank at Burnham Grammar School. It subsequently never grew back.

Favourite band is Ace of Base.

Her mother always refers to her as 'Cow'.

Has a pet reindeer.

Guests

Alice Beer
Alice is a grade one, numero uno, first-rate lunatic, who can often be found crawling on all fours up her local high street in a ballet outfit, collecting worms to throw at the British Telecom shop.

Hale ...
Plumptious, bum-faced Norman invented the hot cross bun when he dropped a red-hot crucifix onto a currant bun. Fiercely jealous of his partner Gareth's looks, Norman has injected over 40,000 pounds of collagen into his face.

... and Pace
Bulbous-headed, cat-faced Gareth grew his moustache in an attempt to look gay. He's not of course... No! In fact he's a macho robotics dance teacher. He can often be seen sweating like a pig in his local scout hut whilst eager young cubs bottle up his perspiration and sell it as beer which, to all intents and purposes, it is.

Martine McCutcheon
Martine, who plays pot lady Tiffany in EastEnders may appear to be as common as muck but is in fact more posh than the Queen. She demanded that her dressing room be filled with crowns, golden goblets, precious stones, jewels and prizes beyond your wildest dreams. Whilst she bathed she was fed peacock feathers by two 30-stone, blind, completely nude, Welsh eunuchs.

Rose-Marie

Pudding faced baker's daughter Rose-Marie has a magnificent pair of front buns which she soaks all day in linseed oil in preparation for the hammering they take each night from her husband's cricket bat.

Noah Huntley

Dashing biker Noah was once the wild man down on *Emmerdale*. He says he's a massive hit with girls. Hmmm ... I'm not so sure, I think he's going to fill out and become quite a porker ... oink, oink, oink, oink. You know, like a pig.

Richard Whiteley

Richard doesn't push his weight around. He doesn't display his muscular frame on the beach or the gym. He doesn't parade around his estate with his chest puffed out in defiance. He doesn't need to ... he's the fastest jazz guitarist in the land.

Caroline Aherne

Buxom, matronly comedienne Caroline has a kind of Uri Geller-style skill. If she rubs her bosoms together a ghost appears from her cleavage and does the Dance of the Seven Onions on a tea towel before popping a sixpence in her hat.

Martin Clunes

Trout-faced comedy actor Martin was one of our favourite guests. The very idea of Martin seems far-fetched. You see, at birth he was simply a head with a leaf for a body. But excellent surgery, supervised by a collie dog, cured him and the only clue to his botanical past is his penchant for chlorophyll.

A day in the life

of George Dawes

'7 am. I get up in the morning and I see the beauty of the leaves upon the trees that glisten in the pleasant, sun-kissed breeze and then I do a poo.'

'It's not easy being a baby. Oh no, Mama. One often spends upwards of four hours a day dealing with correspondence. Many letters contain unsolicited gifts of money. All these gifts have to be accounted for and I usually write a letter of thanks to the sender in my best writing on some RSPCA headed paper that Ulrikakaka gave me for my birthday.'

'Lunch is at 12.30 pm prompt and at 1.15 pm, having watched an episode of *Tots TV* on my twin-speed Fisher Price video, I ring the bell to inform my staff that I am now officially 'at home' and that guests may now be received.'

'Unsurprisingly, the visitors' queue is long. Loud and restless. On a typical day, guests might include Sir Peter Ustinov, Stephen Fry and D-D Dixon.'

'3 pm. It's time to go out on my afternoon rounds. Often I will open a few hospitals. I do wish these doctors would stop forgetting their keys. Ha ha ha ha ha ha ha ha ha that was a good joke.'

'Wasn't that a good joke?'

'4.30 pm, and time for a brief feed. My chef, Rusty Lee is fairly consistent but occasionally the food sucks-rancid-dog's-fat-cock big time. I rarely complain, instead I wait awhile and then, without any fuss, quietly pop out for a KFC. If Rusty challenges me, my response is swift and equivocal: 'YOU DON'T KNOW NUFFIN!'

'6.15 pm. It's time for a wee and a poo and a bath. If time is short, I tend to combine all three.'

'6.30 pm. I go to bed.'

'9.45 pm. Some tykes are throwing stones at my window and wake me up. Pulling back the *Pingu* curtains I discover that the tykes are indeed Mr Mortimer and Mr Reeves and the stones are in fact Smarties. I eat the Smarties, slide down the pipe on the outside of my house and join the pair.'

'10.15 pm, The Bentley arrives outside the nightclub and we all go in and meet women.'

'6.58 am. I step out of the Bentley and climb up the pipe. I get into bed and enjoy a blissful sleep before the new day dawns.'

Guests

Simon Bates

Gentle, gormless giant Simon spends his weekends lumbering around the kitchen crushing ants with his thumb. When he believes they are all gone, he stares out of the window at his rotting paddling pool, which reminds him of the days before the ants came.

Carol Smilie

Bumptious, bra-buster, brainbox Carol looks great in tights whatever the denier. She is often seen driving around the Highlands in her motorized top hat looking for piglets to castrate with her razor-sharp teeth.

Russell Grant

Harmless, rotund cherub Russell specializes in celestial hocus-pocus, astral rumours and horoscopic jiggery-pokery. When not pedalling his preposterous planetary predictions, he sits alone in his bungalow weaving lace curtains until the gallons of camomile tea he consumes take effect. He then drifts into a deep astral slumber where his prophecies once again take root.

Samantha Janus

Anaemic, unemployed milkmaid Samantha, despite being a hefty fifteen-and-a-half stone, is no slouch and can regularly be seen sprinting up the M1 to see where it leads.

Chris Rea
Bulky, bad-tempered, lumbering, gravel-voiced man-mountain Chris dyes his hair four times a day with a mixture more usually found in pies. When not smoking weeds, he can often be found laughing at monkey posters in his four-acre nineteenth-century khazi.

Gary Rhodes
Punk cook Gary owns a café in central London where he boils food in old tin baths and serves it up to the capital's hoi polloi in reclaimed concrete horse troughs. He achieves his unique hairstyle by suspending himself bat-style over a steaming pot of egg albumen every night.

Syd Little
Slim, suave, sophisticated, four-eyed fanny-magnet Syd is a sort of comedian. Despite his slender frame he eats like a pig. Syd doesn't need to wear specs, he just likes the look. He says, 'It makes me look just like Buddy Holly.' What do you think?

Eddie Large
Podgy, funbucket and Danny-Baker-look-alike Eddie likes nothing better than making love on a rug in front of a roaring open fire. Sadly Eddie now lives in a tower block and it's just not the same in front of a radiator.

Interview with Ulrika Jonsson

Bob: Ulrika, welcome to *London in the Afternoon*. Here is my colleague Vic Reeves with a few questions.

Vic: What colour's your hair normally?

Ulrika: A sort of aubergine.

Vic: Blacky-purple?

Ulrika: No, I was very blond when I was little although I was born with a receding hairline much like yours, Mr Reeves.

Vic: Well you're doing well in covering it up at the moment. Brush it forward is what I would advise.

Bob: Do you prefer a beach holiday or the countryside?

Ulrika: I like a beach holiday.

Bob: If you were caravanning would you park your caravan at the top of a cliff looking down at the beach, or at the bottom so you could look up?

Ulrika: I wouldn't own a fucking caravan because they're a disgrace.

Bob: Really, what have you got against caravans?

Ulrika: Stiffies own caravans.

Vic: 'Stiffies own caravans'. Can you elaborate on that?

Bob: What exactly is a 'stiffie'? We'd like to know.

Ulrika: I haven't seen one in a long time but they're drips.

Jim: A stiffie that drips.

Ulrika: It's an awful, awful life.

Bob: Do you have any skin problems?

Ulrika: A touch of ringworm.

Bob: No eczema or anything like that?

Ulrika: I used to but it's all cleared up.

Bob: Did you find you didn't have many friends?

Ulrika: Well, it was just the ringworm that put people off.

Vic: It can drive people away in flocks.

Bob: Can you remember a particularly nice birthday present you've had?

Ulrika:	Yes, I was once given a little glittery hat like Agnetha from Abba wore when she sang 'Waterloo'.
Vic:	I remember. Was that your favourite hat?
Ulrika:	No, my Uri Geller hat is my favourite hat.
Vic:	And that's a magic hat?
Ulrika:	It's empowered me and given me things.
Bob:	Are people in Sweden proud of Abba?
Ulrika:	Yes.
Vic:	Have you ever met them?
Ulrika:	I would like to one day.
Vic:	Which one? One of them looks like a mouse doesn't he?
Ulrika:	Yes, that's Bjorn. He looks like a hamster I think.
Vic:	Well, a hamster-rat.
Bob:	Are digital clocks on the way out?
Ulrika:	They're just coming in aren't they?
Vic:	In your world they may well be but in the rest of the world they've been around quite some years now.
Bob:	Do you get to sleep easily at night?
Ulrika:	Tend to, yes.
Vic:	You don't have any peacocks around that keep you awake?
Ulrika:	No, but next-door's television's very loud.
Vic:	Have you complained?
Ulrika:	Sort of.
Vic:	Directly or via the police or the Noise Abatement Society? I find the Noise Abatement Society the most effective. I've had them round to complain to some peacocks and a cuckoo.
Ulrika:	I saw two pigeons making love yesterday.
Vic:	Were they in bed together?
Ulrika:	They were on this fence and the male one mounted the female one and he went 'Ffffffffff' and then he got off her and she went 'cooooooooooo'.
Bob:	Cor, that was lovely, mate.
Vic:	And did he have a fag then?
Ulrika:	Yes, on the television aerial.
Vic:	Had a fag and a glass of wine.
Bob:	What do you think of Mark Lamarr?
Ulrika:	Miserable bastard.
Vic:	Would you like to do him in?
Ulrika:	I'd like to fucking nut him, punch him hard in the face, a few on the arms, knee him in the groin, a half-nelson down on the floor and then garotte him.
Vic:	What do you think of George the lovely baby?
Ulrika:	Very nice – I like George.
Vic:	Is he cuddlesome?
Ulrika:	I might like to pat his head.
Vic:	That's all, you wouldn't go any further?
Ulrika:	No, not at this early stage.
Vic:	Let your relationship develop.
Bob:	Well, Ulrika, thank you very much. Enjoy your stay in London.

How Ulrika transformed

Bearded Troll

herself

from a Bearded Troll to a Beauty

Beauty

Dove top 20 hits

1	Dove me Coo	The Beatles
2	Under the Coo of Dove	Showaddywaddy
3	Hand in Dove	The Smiths
4	I Dove to Dove	Tina Charles
5	Feather Give up on a Good Wing	Alex O'Neal
6	Crazy for Coo	Madonna
7	How Deep is your Dove	Bee Gees
8	I'm not in Dove	10 C.C.
9	Without Coo	Harry Nilsson
10	Radar Dove	Golden Earring
11	Whole Lotta Dove	Led Zeppelin
12	Coo to me are Every Wing	Imagination
13	Baby Dove	Coopremes
14	Dovely Day	'Bill' Withers
15	Everlasting Dove	Dove Affair
16	(You're simply) The Nest	Tina Turner
17	You're the Nest Wing (that feather happened coo me)	Style Council
18	Crazy Little Wing Called Dove	Queen
19	Fly Wing-a-Wing	Chuck Berry
20	Hot Dove	T.Rex

Mark's hair-do

Why does he do it?

Mark has created a ghee-based (butter) lump on the top of his head. We can only speculate as to why. Here are some thoughts:

1   He is retarded.

2   He has an unusually frequent need for lubrication:

to dislodge his head from between the school railings;
to remove the Eddie Cochran bangles from his wrists;
to oil the chain on his Renco hot-dog warmer;
to ease his counterfeit coins into fruit machines;
to fry eggs on his head during a heatwave;
to effect lack of grip on a bottle of frightening sauce;
to trap winged insects for his rocking robin.

3   He needs to create a humid atmosphere on his head to encourage parsley growth, which he still believes to be subject to rationing.

4   He wishes to look common.

5   It is not hair at all but external veins which he must disguise to avoid being shunned by all those who keep their veins internally.

6   He believes it attracts ladies' attention away from his rubber lips and rather whimsical manner.

7   He needs the extra weight of the ghee to counterbalance his pendulous breasts.

8   He hides his counterfeit banknotes beneath its impenetrable shell.

9   It is used to deflect headbutts.

Turn the page to see how to recreate Mark's hair-do.

Mark's hair-do – How does he do it?

1   Mark has finished his tea of boiled beef and carrots and retires to his bedroom to prepare for the 'hop' at the local village hall.

2   Each individual hair is bathed in a bucket of three-in-one oil.

3   The scalp is cooled using a firearm that has been kept in the fridge.

4   The scalp is then rubbed with emery paper to provide grip for the ghee.

5   Two packs of Lurpak, one of Anchor, two of Kerrygold and one of Cookeen are gently melted over an Elvis memorial candle inside a replica of the clock that Bill Haley rocked around.

6   The heated ghee is placed inside an empty Flora tub and then the entire head is covered with frozen bullets until the ghee re-solidifies.

7   The ghee lump is then shaped using a butter knife.

8   Finally the ghee (butter) is re-clarified by placing the head 6 inches away from Mark's neon 'Elvisely Yours' lamp.

9   Mark dons his drapes and jitterbugs down to the village hall, where once again he is the only one who turns up.

Guests

Bill Oddie
Ugly Bill, the birdspotter, lives in a nest high on a cliff at a secret location. Since he became a protected species, his eggs are guarded 24 hours a day by a team of armed binmen.

Caryn Franklin
Gaunt, hollow-cheeked, mouse-faced Caryn can't remember the last time she did an honest day's work. That's because she can't remember anything due to drink. She did, however, remember to turn up, which was surprising as she wasn't invited.

Annabel Giles
Feisty, mean-faced rumour-monger and gossip Annabel is 50 years old. She says she keeps herself looking younger by eating mud, but to be honest, we think she looks 50 years old ... and the rest.

Richard Wermerling
Richard came up with the name for his pop group Let Loose whilst lying in bed one night after enjoying a few plates of marrowfat peas. Richard is a self-confessed simpleton and spends his days burying soil in allotments.

Jonathan Ross
Big-boned Jonathan Ross weighs 17 stone but that's not fat. Oh no, he's just big-boned with a healthy supplement of good old British muscle. And those chins? Well, they're just shadows caused by the studio lighting.

Stephen Fry
Huge, lumbering hulk Stephen is often seen loping around Mayfair in search of lost monocles, discarded dancing canes and mislaid duelling pistols. Why, even now I can see him eyeing up my topper.

Wolf
The Wolf may not be a real wolf. We just don't know at this stage. He gained his name because he produces dog dirt and spends his days gnawing on bones in his kennel. Nice one, Wolf. Howooooooo.

Leslie Ash
Lovely, pretty Leslie. Sweet, soft-skinned, lovely Leslie. Kind, warm, graceful Leslie. Delicate Leslie. Dainty Leslie. Oh Leslie. Elegant, elf-like, sweet-smelling Leslie. Oh lovely Leslie. Oh Leslie.

Sam Beckinsale
Shy Sam loves cats. She feeds them on butter, cream, Scottish shortbread, dancing slippers, sultanas and Needlers York Fruits until they reach four stone. Then she slaughters them and eats them as a luxury-dairy cat desert.

Mark's

bedroom

Interview with George Dawes

Bob: Well, George, welcome to *London in the Afternoon* with Mr Vic Reeves and me, Mr Bob Mortimer.

Vic: You're a very good drummer, George. Who bought you your drum kit?

George: Rusty Lee.

Bob: Who taught you to play or are you self-taught?

George: Self-taught.

Bob: What's your favourite drum speed?

George: 4/4 or 16/8.

Bob: Now, tell us about your parents, George.

George: Ah now it's interesting, I didn't think we would allude to parentage.

Bob: Any brothers or sisters?

George: No. I'm not really of this earth, if the truth be known.

Vic: Do you believe in Martians?

George: No but I believe in marshes. I like spending time in marshland and bogland.

Bob: Who's your favourite celebrity pin-up?

George: Jason Bateman out of *Teenwolf Two*.

Vic: Are you ready for the invasion of the cartoon Saxons?

George: When they start coming for me I will jump into my computer and I will fight them and I will win. I beat the Vikings and I can take the Saxons on any day.

Bob: I think everybody is aware that we are due to be invaded by the salt people. What are you going to do when they land on our shores?

Vic: Do you know how to destroy salt people?

Bob: You spray them with a hose-pipe and it turns them into brine, then you simply drink them and they're gone.

Vic:	How long can you watch cartoons for?
George:	Weeks on end if I'm not in nightclubs smoking cigarettes with Sarah Ferguson.
Bob:	Do you get in free?
George:	Yes, I know Major Ron Ferguson and he puts in a word.
Bob:	Which is your favourite nightclub?
George:	Stringfellow's probably.
Bob:	Do you like Peter Stringfellow?
George:	Yes. You had him on the show didn't you?
Vic:	Did you meet him then?
George:	Yes, I asked him if he would give me some of his money.
Vic:	And did he?
George:	Yes.
Vic:	How much?
George:	Fiver.
Bob:	Five squid?
George:	I had to give him something in return.
Vic:	What?
George	Well, he told me I wasn't allowed to tell.
Vic:	Are you in whatever way, shape or form, or have you ever been, magic?
George:	Yes.
Vic:	What magic skills do you have? Can you make yourself invisible?
George:	I can fly.
Bob:	Over great distances?
George:	No.
Bob:	Over grapes?
George:	Yes, and plantations. I can make it rain. I'm a witch doctor.
Vic:	Have you ever drowned?
George:	I drown most Thursdays. Mary Poppins tries to drown me.
Vic:	Do you ever feel you want to get into the sea, find out where the lobsters live and spend a bit of time with them?
George:	Yes, well I try and relive the life of *The Water Babies*.
Vic:	I know you like tartan, George. What exactly is that? A check?
George:	I like the lines and the way they cross each other. I have tartan wallpaper. I'd rather have tartan than *Pingu* which they tried to make me have.
Bob:	Do you not like *Pingu?*
George	No, I hate him.
Vic:	Have you ever got dressed up in a tight gymkhana outfit?
George:	Yes, when I tried out for the Russian shotputting team.
Vic:	And did it affect your performance?
George:	Yes, it certainly enhanced my performance.
Vic:	I think you look very suave in your hunting outfit, if you don't mind me saying.
George:	Well, that's what ladies like in a baby.
Bob:	What would you like to be when you grow up?
George:	An airline pilot.
Bob:	Thank you, George.

Guests

Tommy Cannon
Tommy who plays the part of the Cannon and Bobby who plays the Ball, were originally called Pea and Shooter but as their popularity grew the size of the weaponry increased. The one displayed here is the cannon.

Paul Shane
Heavyweight shandy-drinker Paul travels everywhere by pogo stick. However, he makes life difficult for himself because he insists on sitting on the top deck of the buses and it can take hours for him to negotiate the stairs on his stick. Regardless of that, he is a chirpy beefcake of a man who, during the recording, occasionally issued a high-pitched peeling fart.

Bobby Ball
Bobby sits alone all day on his mountain throne looking down benignly on the residents of Huddersfield. He tugs gently on his bright-red trouser harness in the forlorn hope that he might be called down from the mountain to fight for Huddersfield against Bradford's own mountain guardian, Vic Feathers.

Richard E. Grant
Poppy-out-eyed reptilian-thespian Richard prances around his village green in an Elizabethan ruff and beige pantaloons reciting Shakespearean drivel in his booming RADA-style sweary voice to frighten children. When he is exhausted he rushes back to the reptile house at London Zoo for his 5 o'clock feeding.

Robbie Williams

Ex-heart-throb Robbie is made up of over 90 per cent pork. Known locally as 'The Porklord' he porks his car in a high-rise car pork. Robbie arrived on a one-mile-high motorized coconut, descended from its hairy husk on a hydraulic 'Daliesque' lip sofa and then launched himself directly on to the studio floor astride his one-eyed sausage-dog machine ... nice one, Robbie!

Peter Stringfellow

Peter is well known and admired for his lustrous hair, perfect complexion and disco! Known around town as 'Disco Dick' – the dick with a disco – Peter dances like a little monkey then returns home at dawn to cry himself to sleep on his *Thomas the Tank Engine* lilo. He left in a motorized disco-coffin, after trampling the *Blue Peter* garden and dancing on Petra's grave.

Dermot Morgan

Silvery-haired Dermot likes nothing more than relaxing in front of an open fire picking stuff off his pet labrador's belly, rolling it into little pellets and throwing them out of his window. The mound is now so tall and sweaty, it has caused his neighbour's tomatoes to wilt.

Shane Richie

Cheese-faced, lily-livered, spineless-gork Shane absolutely worships puddings, so much so that he's the new vicar at St Pecan-in-the-Pie. He arrived at Shooting Stars on his BMX. He took great precautions by locking this up with a variety of Chubb locks. Unfortunately he attached it to Dennis Waterman's Sea King helicopter which took off, taking Dennis home to his castle.

Things you didn't even know about ...

George

1   George was not the first choice for score master in *Shooting Stars*. Wincey Willis was approached first but was unable to partake on account of her being up the duff.

2   For his birthday, George received a *Pingu* book, a *Pingu* video and another *Pingu* book.

3   George's favourite band is teen sensation *Upside Down*. He says 'I like Giles Kristian the best'.

4   George Dawes done a poo in the girls' toilets.

5   Since 1953, George has been spending upwards of 3d a week on magazines of a nefarious nature. These magazines are kept in Lamarr's shed where they now rot like a small dead man.

6   Like Vanilla Ice, George 'from the streets'.

7   George doesn't even like *Pingu*. He once got a *Pingu* toy and pretended he liked it and now everyone thinks he likes *Pingu*, but he doesn't.

8   George has got a big willy.

9   Honest.

10   George has been known to spend evenings with Lady Diana in nightclubs where he smokes cigarettes.

11   George's worst food is mince.

12   When pushed, George stresses the need for a referendum on Europe, although he is reluctant to declare public support for any individual political party.

13   You is fat cow.

14   George's favourite television memory was 'in *Blue Peter* where the elephant done a poo on the floor and they all fell in the poo and got poo in their hair'.

Dawes

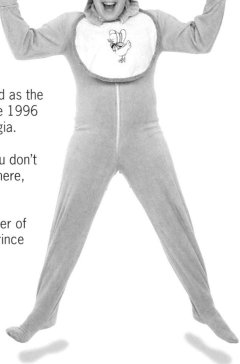

15 If George won the lottery, he would hire a hitman to kill *Pingu*.

16 In a fight, George believes he could have Noel and Liam Gallagher without too much trouble. George says, 'A swift blow to the head and then a knee in the groin. I've already done that Jarvis and taking Damon out was child's play.'

17 George is insistent that the whole 'baby' thing is behind him, although he still secretly longs to have The Great Suprendo visit him with sweets and magic.

18 When Arsenal win a match, George dances upon rooftops and he keeps on until someone has a nasty accident.

19 George Dawes admires scousers for their adorable sense of humour.

20 George's celebrated duet with Monserrat Caballo has been adopted as the official theme tune for the 1996 Atlanta Olympics in Georgia.

21 According to George, 'You don't have to be mad to work here, but it helps!'

22 George's favourite member of the royal family is HRH Prince Philip. 'He is nice,' says George.

23 Hallo.

What the stars keep in their

Chris Tarrant

Rifle
Ceremonial sword and cape
Skin whitener
Hair music
Madness pills
Mashed potato in a sock
Greyhound embryo
Death threat from Lord Snowdon

Bob Geldof

Eighty carrots
Biodegradable harp

Anthea Turner

Leg splints
Wedding sponge
Part of a nipple
Aubergine with 'grief' written on it
Downers
Baby fly nursery

Harry Secombe

Squatters' Rights handboo
Mogadon
Ditherers' clubcard
Willberries
Squits tablets
Lead comb
Soiled tights
Blockbuster card

handbags

Richard Branson
- Cakes
- Balloons
- Maps
- Pencil donkey
- Friendship bracelet
- Hedex
- Harbour-master's report
- Spare belly ring

Murray Walker
- Beetroot seeds
- Shooters
- Multi-purpose hook
- Jam-pot covers
- Sweet mice
- Plan of Lassiters
- CS gas
- Cosh

Björk
- Kidney beans
- Oven doves
- Test tube of polar-bear blood
- Milk gloves
- Sun hat
- Pulsating crab heart
- Plaster of Harris

Guests

Muriel Grey
Dour, thin-lipped, elf-like-Scot Muriel is one of the best fighters in the Highlands. She attacks randomly, without just cause, and recently hacked a bloke's spine out with a chicken bone simply for wearing his trilby skewwhiff.

David Baddiel
Cloven-hoofed David has a spare bell attached to his cobblers. His body is made entirely of worms and the Dutch use him as a landing strip for their flying kettles.

Gabrielle
Gabrielle is never happier than when she's rolling around on her tummy-tum-tum, colouring in the pictures in her *Pocahontas* sketchbook and nibbling on her giant marzipan ball. She then rises, bows to the crowd and leaves the stage.

Danny Baker

Clammy, dripping, sticky Danny has spent his life fighting a losing battle against sweat. At his peak he was producing an average of 16 gallons an evening, causing his neighbours to dub him 'Aqua Dan the Sweating Man'. He has, however, made his fortune selling the stuff as 'Bakerlite', the Greek morning drink.

Julia Carling

Julia has an elaborate draining system carved into her back to drain off all the cats that come out of her mind. They are syphoned off into a cooling bucket attached to her award-winning arse and, when sufficiently chilled, she devours them with onions and so the process begins again.

Patsy Palmer

Reptilian, red-haired Patsy is so freckly that at school she was nicknamed the 'Whitechapel Dalmatian'. One day, however, she joined the dots on her forearm to find they spelt *EastEnders*. She knew then that she was destined to a life grazing on rubbery cockles and whelks and participating in endless knees-up.

Les Dennis

Recently potty-trained Les is never happier than when he's boiling eggs and hiding them around the home. Sadly he can never remember where he's put them and it takes matron hours to console him, sponging him down again and again until he has calmed down and can commence boiling again.

☆ 62 ☆

Shooting Stars ... The Game

How to Play the Game

Object of the game
The object is to play one whole game of *Shooting Stars*. The game consists of five rounds. The player with the most points at the end of the game is the winner.

Setting Up
Before playing the game, cut the game playing board and counters out from the back of the book. You will also needa clock or watch with a second hand.

Rules of the game
The question master may only respond to an answer with 'Eranu', for a correct answer, or 'Uvavu', for an incorrect answer. These can be found on tracks 47 and 48 of the *Shooting Stars* CD. If the question master gives any other response, one point must be deducted from their score.Before starting the game the players must decide whether they are going to pre-select a punishment for the loser or whether the winner will select one at the end of the game. Suggested punishments are given on page 118.

Round One: True or False
The youngest player is the first to take their turn as question master. The question master should turn to the True or False section of the book (page 66) and ask a randomly selected question to the player on their left. The player receives one point for a correct answer. The question master then passes the book to their left. The round continues until each player has received a question.

Round Two: Impressions
Again, the youngest player is the first question master. The question master should turn to the Impressions section of the book (page 74) and ask the player on their left to choose a number between 1 and 99 to select a celebrity, and a number between 1 and 122 to select a phrase. The player

must then do an impression of this celebrity, saying the chosen phrase. The player is awarded three points for a superb impression, one point for an average impression and no points for an embarrassing mess. The book is then passed to the left until each player has done an impression.

Round Three: Club Singer/Part One
Insert the *Shooting Stars* CD into your CD player. The CD contains 46 songs sung by Vic in the club style. Each player, beginning with the youngest, must listen to a randomly selected song and guess the song title. You can select the song by choosing a number between 1 and 46 or by using the random function on your CD player. The answer is given following the song, so be careful to stop the CD. The player scores two points for correctly identifying song. If this player answers incorrectly then the player on his left may have a guess and so on.

Club Singer/Part Two
Each player, beginning with the youngest, must sing a song in the club style from the Club Singer section of the book (page 80). If the song is correctly guessed by any player, then the singing player gets one point. The singer must choose a number between 1 and 112 to select their song. If no one can identify the song, but when its title is revealed all the players agree that it was identifiable, then the singing player gets three points. If all the players agree that it was impossible to identify, the singing player loses one point.

Round Four: Dove from Above
Again, each player takes a turn at being the question master and the play moves to the left. The question master turns to the Dove from Above section (page 86) and asks the player on their left to choose a number between 1 and 221 to select a question. This player receives two points for a correct answer. If another player feels they know the answer, then they must commence cooing like a dove. The first player to coo has the first chance to answer in event of a pass or an incorrect answer, the second player to coo has the second chance, and so on. If a player interrupts without cooing, one point is deducted from their score.

Round Five: Quick Fire
Begin this round by playing track 49 of the *Shooting Stars* CD. Each player asks three questions randomly selected from the Quick Fire questions section (page 98). If there are three or more players, then the first player to shout 'Ulrikakaka' gets the first chance to answer, the second player to shout 'Ulrikakaka' gets the second chance, and so on. A player receives two points for a correct answer and loses two points for an incorrect answer.

At the end of the game
The player with most points is the winner. The player with least is the loser and must partake of a punishment. This punishment may be pre-selected by all the players or be chosen by the winner. In the Punishments section of the book (page 118) you will find some of our suggestions, but feel free to devise your own ... anything from snogging grandad or grandma or doing the washing-up to eating an eggshell or standing nude in the garden shed for five minutes.

Once you have become over-familiar with the club singer CD you may omit Part One of Round Three. If you wish to play a longer game, simply repeat Rounds One to Five as many times as you wish.

True or False

The youngest player is the first to take their turn as question master. The question master asks a randomly selected question to the player on their left. The player receives one point for a correct answer. The question master then passes the book to their left. The round continues until each player has received a question.

Adolf Hitler enjoyed eating chocolate cake covered with whipped cream and topped with a chocolate swastika. *T*

While getting soaked during his classic dance routine in *Singing in the Rain*, Gene Kelly was suffering from flu. *T*

Jean-Claude Van Damme lost the part of the monster in the movie *Predator*, after he complained that his costume was too tight. *T*

The only creature to have one eye is the one-eyed trouser snake. *F*

Jerry Garcia was a well-known tie designer. *T*

Eskimos have their teeth removed at birth to avoid them chattering in the cold and thus giving away their whereabouts to polar bears. *F*

Claudia Schiffer has a pet guinea fowl, which can jump from her shoulder on to David Copperfield's. *F*

Tim Brooke-Taylor's father invented the tea bag. *F*

Every day in the UK 40 people go blind. *T*

A human adult produces enough sweat in one year to fill a bath. *T*

Nick Owen once went home from TV-AM in weather-girl Wincey Willis' underwear. *T*

The father of *Blockbusters* presenter, Bob Holness, taught King Solomon of the Zulus how to drive. *T*

Peacocks can be heard ejecting large audible farts in stately homes around the UK. *F* – their farts are inaudible to humans.

Hares are the only other mammal that can run over 100 metres on two feet. *F*

Comedian Frank Skinner took his name from a member of his dad's domino team. *T*

In elephant dentistry, zoologists often use dynamite to extract their teeth. *F*

Asteroid 4442 has been renamed 'Garcia' in honour of Jerry Garcia of the Grateful Dead. *T*

When *Neighbours* first began, the budget was so small that the dress designer had to buy clothes from Oxfam to dress stars like Kylie. *T*

Ronan from Boyzone used to run for Ireland. *T*

At the beginning of his career Martin Clunes played a *Dr Who* villain who wore a blue dress and was possessed by an evil snake. *T*

In medieval times, pigeon vomit was used to make shoes and gloves waterproof. *F*

Krakatau is actually west of Java. *T*

The Antarctic is much colder than the Arctic. *T*

Tramps have a higher testosterone level, on average, than standard people. *F*

Kate Moss is the daughter of Kevin Moss, one of the Moss Brothers dress-hire people. *F*

Tommy Vance achieves his lovely, deep growling voice by eating rich Christmas cake every day of the year. *F*

Rice paper is not made from rice. *T*

The wall cavities at Broadcasting House are filled with eelgrass. *T*

The London Underground was originally steam driven. *T*

The first motorist to be convicted of speeding in this country was travelling at eight miles per hour. *T*

On the Beatles' song 'Yellow Submarine', the submarine effects were made by John blowing bubbles through a straw and George swirling water in a bucket. *T*

Yellow canaries can be made to change colour by tampering with their food. *T*

The sap from a crab-apple tree is a pig aphrodisiac. *F*

The first fairground merry-go-rounds used real stuffed horses. *F*

Chop suey is actually an American dish. *T*

The most popular colour for a car is blue or grey. *T*

Normally, a right-handed person's left foot is bigger than their right. *T*

One ripe tomato placed among green ones will help them turn red. *T*

Tomatoes are poisonous to cats. *F*

The most popular name for newborn boys in remote Nepalese villages is Eddie Fisher. *T*

The longest word in the English language contains nearly two thousand letters. *T*

Beetroot has to be pickled or cooked because if it is eaten raw it causes eye discoloration. *F*

Before the invention of razors men often shaved with frozen mangetout. *F*

The product most exported from the UK is the same as that most imported. *T*

The jacuzzi was named after the man who invented it. *T*

The 'T' in Ice T stands for tea towel. *F*

The 'T' in James T Kirk stands for teacake. *F*

Ostriches can see through soil to a depth of approximately 10 inches. *F*

The square most landed on in a game of Monopoly is Trafalgar Square. *T*

The Blackpool Tower was first built in Manchester. *T*

The smallest country in the world is less than half a square kilometre. *T*

Short pianist Jools Holland has webbed feet. *T*

Melanie Griffiths has a ripe pear tattooed on her right buttock. *T*

Sam Goldwyn's real name was Sam Goldfish. *T*

Gloria Estefan was taught in a convent by a really fat nun with a moustache. *T*

For the last three years Debbie Daniels has had a live ant living inside her veins cleaning the bacteria deposited there by Paul's magic. *F*

Alfred Hitchcock loved train timetables so much that he used to memorize them. *T*

Martin Sheen was born with his left arm three inches shorter than his right. *T*

Debbie Greenwood has the largest gopher farm in the UK, called Greenwood's Goofy Gophers. *F*

Bruce Forsyth's first catch phrase was, 'I'll have another apple, matron.' *F*

On his passport, Marlon Brando's occupation is 'shepherd'. *T*

Clint Eastwood was sacked by Universal Studios because his Adam's apple was too prominent. *T*

Director Steven Spielberg swallowed a transistor at the age of 15. *T*

A literal translation of Gerard Depardieu is 'Oh my God'. *T*

Walt Disney's head is cryogenically preserved, awaiting future medical advances. *T*

Guinea fowls' eggs are laid already hard-boiled. *F*

Pavarotti has two stomachs: one for food and one for drink. *F*

The boy Russell Grant can see into the future. *T*

The dancer Nijinsky was the inventor of an ever-sharp pencil. *T*

Ulrika Jonsson made three months-worth of annoying calls to a neighbour before being caught. *T*

Queeen Elizabeth I was petrified of roses. *T*

David Soul performed as a singer in the sixties with a paper bag over his head. *T*

A heron's beak is longer than a Curly Wurly. *T*

Sammy Davis Jr was blinded during a fight with Frank Sinatra when Sinatra thrust a biro into his eye. *F*

Charlie Chaplin suffered from brittle elbows, which meant he could never row a boat. *F*

Randy Newman had special foam hip units built so he could stand upright in his swimming pool singing songs of woe to passers-by. *F*

The group Everything But the Girl are named after a bridal shop. *T*

The planets have a direct influence over our lives. *F*

A shoe becomes a boot when its upper reaches above the ankle. *F*

Ben Nevis is named after a Scottish hermit who is alleged to have owned the mountain in days gone by. *F*

The dog that played *Lassie* in the movies had to wear a wig to cover his genitals as Lassie was supposed to be a girl and the dog which played the role was a boy. *T*

Bare-knuckle fist fighters are known to wrap their hands in haddock skins on the evening preceding a fight. *F*

If a bell is not rung on last orders in a pub, then you are legally entitled to a free pint. *F*

Human hair makes a powerful anti-arthritis potion if boiled in hot milk. *F*

The longest human hair ever recorded was 15 metres long. *F*

Although human hair can be bleached by acids there is no known acid that can actually dissolve it. *F*

Comparing a person to a recent photograph is a far more accurate means of identification than DNA testing. *F*

A rope made from human hair was used to lower the guns of Navarone to their cliff-side nest. *F*

Valerie Singleton was caught by an airship sunbathing topless on the secluded balcony of her flat. *T*

There is a move in judo where the recipient of the blow reaches instant orgasm, leaving them wide open to attack. *F*

A boomerang is the Australian equivalent of a blunt knife. *F*

With his shoes on, John Cleese is an inch short of being medically classified as a giant. *T*

Mark Lamarr achieves his unique hairstyle with the copious application of treacle. *F*

Sheena Easton has two very fat thumbs, which means her coats have to be buttoned up by someone else. *F*

Mr Bean is the inspiration for a new dance craze in Jamaica where dancers adopt a ludicrous walk and act like a nerd. *T*

There is no cream in a cream cracker. *T*

A red port-wine stain on the face can be removed with white wine or lemon. *F*

Honey bees are very wary of jam. *T*

Elizabeth Hurley got so drunk on Cydrax once that she vowed in the future only to drink Peardrax. *F*

Live snakes are used as belts by some Hindus. *F*

Cloth caps were originally worn by Lancashire mill workers to stop silkworms and their droppings falling into their hair. *F*

John Major has every Wednesday morning off so he can read *Melody Maker*. *F*

Weasels are the only mammals who produce offspring that are larger at birth than the adult. *F*

Smoked sausages were originally smoked in the mouth like cigarettes. *F*

Tofu is actually enjoyed as a food in parts of Asia. *F*

A heron's beak is longer than a standard Mars bar. *F*

Buster Crabbe got his name because he bust a crab's back with his rattle when it crawled into his pram. *F*

If you were standing at the equator you would be travelling at 1000 miles per hour. *T*

Spiders have no ears. *T*

High Court judges' wigs used to be so heavy that they were supported by a special brace attached to the judge's chair. *F*

Food has the same amount of calories whether hot or cold. *T*

A rottweiler's jaw pressure is equivalent to a duck eating its way through an oak door. *F*

Nutmeg sprinkled directly on to a human will cause terrible irritation throughout the night. *F*

The legal limit of coppers that shopkeepers are obliged to accept is 20 pence. *T*

Woody Allen eats out 365 days a year. *T*

If a duck had the equivalent leg power to a flea it would be possible for it to jump over the English Channel. *F*

According to EC regulations a potato crisp must not be larger than a male adult human ear. *F*

As well as a vow of celibacy, Methodist ministers take a vow agreeing not to swim in public swimming baths. *F*

Roseanne Barr broke a rabbit's neck when she put it in the washing machine because its feet were dirty. *T*

Eddie Murphy once had to remove two pounds of jewellery to get through an airport metal detector. *T*

Oranges are not the only fruit. *T*

A plain-chocolate digestive is on average one gram heavier than its milk-chocolate equivalent. *F*

The salt residue contained in one year's-worth of human sweat is enough to satisfy the requirements of a provincial chip shop for one month. *F*

Harvey Stephens, who played Damien in *The Omen*, was 26 years old in 1996. *T*

In Sweden carpenters use Ryvita as a fine finishing sandpaper. *F*

Elephants have two hearts. *F*

Cows have two throats. One for grass and one for milk. *F*

Chinese can only grow beards on their chins. *F*

Novelist Jilly Cooper always puts a foul-smelling yellow flower in her shoe when she starts a new novel. *T*

The Romans used a mixture of sand and yoghurt to polish their armour and shields. *F*

The world's largest-selling poster is the one of a monkey on the toilet. *F*

The correct name for Welsh rarebit is Welsh rabbit. *T*

The original yo-yo was a four-pound weight attached to a twenty-foot thong. *T*

The Queen employs someone as the Yeoman Ravenmaster, keeper of the Queen's ravens. *T*

A monument to Frank Zappa has been erected in Vilnius, Lithuania, although there is no connection between the two. Town officials felt sure he would have visited had he not died two years earlier. *T*

Before hairdryers, men used to hire a horse for the afternoon and let the wind do its good work. *F*

Jean-Luc Picard was raised in an aviary by a family of penguins. *F*

Scientists in Japan have invented a motorized mouth for paralysed eunuchs. *F*

In his early years, in order to persuade him to move around on stage more, Michael Jackson was told that someone in the audience was trying to shoot him. *T*

David Gower would never wear white socks when playing for England. *T*

When Abraham Lincoln was shot in a theatre he was watching Laurel and Hardy's first movie. *F*

The weight in pollen that a bumblebee can carry is the equivalent to a sparrow carrying an acoustic guitar. *F*

The wiping of excrement on public-toilet walls is a signal by aliens in human form for their brothers to come and rescue them. *F*

Impressions

Again, the youngest player is the first question master. The question master asks the player on their left to choose a number between 1 and 99 to select a celebrity, and a number between 1 and 122 to select a phrase. The player must then do an impression of this celebrity saying the chosen phrase. The player is awarded three points for a superb impression, one point for an average impression and no points for an embarrassing mess. The question master then passes the book to their left. The round continues until each player has done an impression.

People to Impersonate

1 Fergie	15 Anthea Turner
2 Ian McCaskill	16 Henry Cooper
3 Frankie Howerd	17 Billy Connolly
4 Cilla Black	18 Jonathan Ross
5 Corporal Jones	19 George Dawes
6 Tetley Tea Folk	20 Clarence Cliff
7 Jimmy Nail	21 Delboy
8 David Attenborough	22 Bob Hoskins
9 Ade Edmondson	23 Robin Day
10 Margaret Thatcher	24 Tommy Cooper
11 Barbara Windsor	25 Barry White
12 Paul Daniels	26 Scooby-Doo
13 Frank Bruno	27 Loyd Grossman
14 Bianca from *EastEnders*	28 Benny Hill

29 Michael Caine	63 Robin Williams
30 Melvyn Bragg	64 Patrick Moore
31 James Mason	65 Gary Barlow
32 Hyacinth Bucket	66 Bernard Breslaw
33 Derek Nimmo	67 Winston Churchill
34 Pavarotti	68 Jimmy Savile
35 John Major	69 Eric Cantona
36 Michael Crawford	70 Bernard Manning
37 Trevor McDonald	71 The Queen
38 David Frost	72 Terry Wogan
39 Mavis from *Coronation St.*	73 Mike Reid
40 Bill Shankly	74 Joe Pasquale
41 The Honey Monster	75 Rik Mayall
42 Joanna Lumley	76 Margi Clarke
43 Björk	77 Ossie Ardiles
44 Princess Di	78 Jimi Somerville
45 Morrissey	79 Mick Jagger
46 Pauline from *EastEnders*	80 Ricky from *EastEnders*
47 Bob Geldof	81 Alf Garnett
48 Nigel Mansell	82 Robert de Niro
49 Bruce Forsyth	83 Dolly Parton
50 The person to your left	84 Paul McCartney
51 Kenneth Williams	85 Michael Jackson
52 Elvis	86 Tonto
53 Cheeta	87 Gordon Brittas
54 Craig Charles	88 Phylis from *Coronation Street*
55 Vera from *Coronation Street*	89 Julian Clary
56 John Inman	90 Rab C. Nesbitt
57 Captain Birdseye	91 Zippy
58 Harry Secombe	92 Cadbury's Caramel Bunny
59 Bugs Bunny	93 The person to your right
60 The person opposite you	94 Victor Meldrew
61 Pam Ayres	95 Darth Vader
62 Sylvester Stallone	96 Cliff Richard

Catch phrases

1 Jeepers, that's a hot potato.

2 Go ahead, punk, make my day.

3 I've got a lovely bunch of coconuts.

4 You gotta be in it to win it.

5 Can you see my baked beans from up there?

6 They call me the gay mountaineer.

7 Please accept this free gift of birdseed (worth £10).

8 I'm Burlington Betty, I rise at 10.30 ... pm!

9 Pump up the jam, pump it up, etc.

10 Pass the dutchy on the left-hand side, and then repeat the manoeuvre on the right until you have mastered it.

11 Down naughty doggy, down, get on your belly, sweet doggy, down.

12 By God, I'm fat.

13 Could I take a likkle peeky-weeky at your winkle.

14 Them buggers at Monkey World should be shot for the way they treated my boy.

15 I'm drowning in a pool of my own droppings.

16 He's a Presbyterian, I'm a eunuch. What a pair!

17 Is this a knife I see in front of me?... oh no, it's my hand.

18 Hey buddy, you don't know jack shit.

19 I'm not a human, I'm an elephant.

20 You don't have to be mad to work here, but it helps.

21 Madam, I am the man who discovered the cure for radishes.

22 I say, this is a sweaty little rabbit hutch.

23 Making love to his eagle, Ziggy chucked up into his wine.

24 My new quiff is good and stiff. You may touch it, if you wish.

25 Where's the pepper pot, Julie?

26 Boiled beef and carrots ... in your dreams.

27 Frankly, my dear, I couldn't give a hand.

28 My eyes, my eyes.

29 Yes sir, I can boogie.

30 Now then, now then, howzabout that then?

31 Hello.

32 I eat sardines and fly like a seagull.

33 Titter ye not, madam.

34 Oh, Betty, the cat's done a widdle on the partridge.

35 My mother-in-law.

36 Eee 'eck you're a lovely couple. Do come back next week and tell us how it went.

37 Hello, good evening and welcome.

38 My husband and I.

39 They don't like it up them.

40 Tetleys make teafolk, make tea for teafolk.

41 Yeah, yeah, yeah. Don't give me the run around, son.

42 Tell them about the honey, mummy.

43 I like it, but not a lot.

44 Jonah was born in a whale.

45 Get off that board, Miss Ford.

46 Nice to see you, to see you nice.

47 You looking at me?

48 Oooh Matron.

49 What's up Doc?

50 Rodney, you are a plonker.

51 Don't you dare go the bookies, our Jack.

52 Ooh shut that door.

53 Just like that.

54 Everyone loves my fishy fingers.

55 I don't believe it.

56 The force is strong in this one.

57 You're a big man but you're out of conditioner.

58 Nanoo Nanoo.

59 Tonight, on the *South Bank Show*.

60 Ooh, I hate you, Butler.

61 We will fight them on the beaches.

62 You silly old moo.

63 Talk about fat, it's ideal for cooking with.

64 Oh dear, these underpants are tight.

65 If someone doesn't blow my nose I'll let it drip on the saveloys.

66 I murdered him because he criticized my cooking.

67 I much prefer young men.

68 Yes, I wear a toupee, it covers my third nipple.

69 Oh no, I've been shafted again.

70 I love mucky books.

71 Can I have two pasties, four sausage rolls and half a pound of pease pudding.

72 Ee, I'm a right dozy git, me.

73 These rubber gloves have started to stink.

74 On an average day I spend five hours in the bookies and the rest in bed watching mucky films.

75 This chicken is rubbery.

76 Yes, my implants are silicone, you silly bitch.

77 I do find the clasps on these earrings a bit fiddly-farty.

78 I've got a lovely bunch of bananas.

79 If you must know, I got the sack for stealing towels.

80 They think it's all over, it is now.

81 You looking at my bra?

82 Hello, the Bucket residence.

83 You'll like this, but not a lot.

84 My other entrance has got a porch.

85 I must admit, I do put it about a bit.

86 Look at the size of that sausage.

87 Kiss me honey honey kiss me.

88 You hum it son, I'll play with it.

89 I'm a big boy now.

90 Nick nick.

91 Let's take a look in the blue kitchen.

92 Bodyform, oh, Bodyform for you.

93 We really want to see those fingers.

94 Mrs Simpson, take your hand off my trumpet.

95 I own several partially disfigured monkeys.

96 I'm finished, mother, come and wipe me.

97 I haven't felt so randy since Barry Crier came in the shop.

98 I'm sorry, Peter, those sultanas are spoken for.

99 You're a fine one to talk, Alistair.

100 I had to shoot him, your honour, he had a forearm.

101 Its more than me knob's worth, mate.

102 These toiletries seem overpriced.

103 Whatever it takes, Ian, I'm desperate.

104 The first boy I ever kissed had a clenched foot.

105 By heck, Colin, you can take a beating.

106 No you're right, Wendy, the left one is higher.

107 Yes, I sell guns, but only at a price.

108 In my experience.

109 I live alone with a hermit.

110 I can't resist putting.

111 Don't ask me, I've got a club foot.

112 My last two wives were both bigheads.

113 I feel like chicken tonight.

114 I think your toaster needs a service, its bleeding beige blood.

115 I don't know about you.

116 That's a dirty habit, Father Brown.

117 Yes my husband beats me, but he never marks my face or glands.

118 Are you running a smear campaign, doctor?

119 It's not easy being a pervert in this country.

120 It's no secret that I am a lager lout.

121 Can I lend your hedge trimmer, Colin, my pubes are caught in my shoe.

122 I feel like a man trapped in a partridge's body.

Club Singer

Part One Insert the *Shooting Stars* CD into your CD player. The CD contains 46 songs sung by Vic in the club style. Each player, beginning with the youngest, must listen to a randomly selected song and guess the song title. You can select the song by choosing a number between 1 and 46 or by using the random function on your CD player. The answer is given following the song, so be careful to stop the CD. The player scores two points for correctly identifying the song. If this player answers incorrectly, then the player on his left may have a guess and so on.

Part Two Each player, beginning with the youngest, must sing a song in the club style from this section of the book. The singer must choose a number between 1 and 112 to select their song. If the song is correctly guessed by any player, then the singing player gets one point. If no one can identify the song, but when its title is revealed all the players agree that it was identifiable, then the singing player gets three points. If all the players agree that it was impossible to identify, the singing player loses one point.

Club singer song suggestions

1	Addicted to Love	Robert Palmer
2	Girls and Boys	Blur
3	All day and All of the Night	The Kinks
4	All my Loving	The Beatles
5	All Shook up	Elvis Presley
6	Babooshka	Kate Bush
7	Can't Buy me Love	The Beatles
8	Crazy	Patsy Cline
9	Nikita	Elton John
10	Ebony and Ivory	McCartney & Wonder

11 Delilah	Tom Jones
12 Fame	Irene Cara
13 For Your Eyes Only	Sheena Easton
14 Goldfinger	Shirley Bassey
15 The Girl from Ipanema	Astrud Gilberto
16 Girls Just Wanna Have Fun	Cyndi Lauper
17 Green Green Grass of Home	Tom Jones
18 The Heat is on	Glenn Frey
19 Harlem Shuffle	Bob & Earl
20 I Shot the Sheriff	Eric Clapton
21 I don't like Mondays	Boomtown Rats
22 I Will Survive	Gloria Gaynor
23 It's Not Unusual	Tom Jones
24 La Bamba	Ritchie Valens
25 Let's Hear it for the Boy	Deniece Williams
26 Let's Stay Together	Al Green
27 Like a Virgin	Madonna
28 My Girl	The Temptations
29 My Way	Frank Sinatra
30 New York/New York	Frank Sinatra
31 9 to 5	Dolly Parton
32 Pretty Woman	Roy Orbison
33 Over the Rainbow	Judy Garland
34 Peggy Sue	Buddy Holly
35 Puppet on a String	Sandie Shaw
36 Que Sera Sera	Doris Day
37 Roxanne	The Police
38 Sentimental Journey	Doris Day
39 Should I Stay or Should I Go	The Clash
40 Singing in the Rain	Various
41 Stand by Me	Ben E King
42 Stop! In the Name of Love	The Supremes
43 Solid	Ashford & Simpson
44 Strangers in the Night	Frank Sinatra

45	Yesterday	The Beatles
46	Surfin USA	The Beach Boys
47	Summer Nights	Newton/Travolta
48	Tainted Love	Soft Cell
49	Take my Breath Away	Berlin
50	Boots are Made for Walking	Nancy Sinatra
51	Ticket to Ride	The Beatles
52	Tutti Frutti	Little Richard
53	Unchained Melody	Righteous Brothers
54	Venus	Bananarama
55	What do you Want	Adam Faith
56	Wild Thing	The Troggs
57	Word Up	Cameo
58	Yellow Submarine	The Beatles
59	You keep me Hangin' on	The Supremes
60	You Can't Hurry Love	Phil Collins
61	You're so Vain	Carly Simon
62	You've Lost that Loving Feeling	Righteous Brothers
63	All out of Love	Air Supply
64	Blue Moon	The Marcels
65	Money Money Money	Abba
66	Bye Bye Love	The Everly Brothers
67	Can't Take my Eyes off of you	Frankie Valli
68	Climb Every Mountain	Shirley Bassey
69	Close to You	The Carpenters
70	The Dock of a Bay	Otis Redding
71	Great Balls of Fire	Jerry Lee Lewis
72	Ferry Across the Mersey	Gerry/Pacemakers
73	Footloose	Kenny Loggins
74	Hello Dolly	Louis Armstrong
75	Staying Alive	The Bee Gees
76	I say a Little Prayer for you	Dionne Warwick
77	Relight my Fire	Take That
78	Total Eclispe of the Heart	Bonnie Tyler

79 It's my Party	Lesley Gore
80 Oh Carol	Neil Sedaka
81 Wonderwall	Oasis
82 Back for Good	Take That
83 Goldeneye	Tina Turner
84 Babe	Take That
85 Atomic	Blondie
86 Sexual Healing	Marvin Gaye
87 Life on Mars	David Bowie
88 Ain't Nobody	Chaka Khan
89 Vienna	Ultravox
90 Wild Wood	Paul Weller
91 Get off	Prince
92 Dancing on the Ceiling	Lionel Richie
93 Streetlife	Randy Crawford
94 Cars	Gary Numan
95 Fire Starter	Prodigy
96 Kiss from a Rose	Seal
97 Club Tropicana	Wham
98 YMCA	Village People
99 My Girl's Mad at Me	Madness
100 Frankie	Sister Sledge
101 Mrs Robinson	Simon & Garfunkel
102 Ride on Time	Black Box
103 Common People	Pulp
104 Rio	Duran Duran
105 Karma Chameleon	Culture Club
106 We are the Champions	Queen
107 Brown Sugar	The Rolling Stones
108 Stay Another Day	East 17
109 Sit Down	James
110 I Wanna be Adored	The Stone Roses
111 The Loco-motion	Little Eva
112 Bad Boys	Wham

1   Go to a swap-meet with a pigeon's beak and return with a box of assorted eyelashes.

2   Draw a picture of the Brecon Beacons with nipples on the two highest peaks.

3   Rip out your heart, fry it lightly in olive oil and return a verdict of insanity.

4   Create an impression of dappled sunshine on your face by painting yellow and black dots on to said face.

Things to do during your

5   Stop a passing car and ask for directions whilst surreptitiously dropping a) one's guts b) a tap into the passenger seat.

6   Go to an empty church and bang on the door shouting, 'The service is appalling here!'

7   Imagine an exotic parrot flying low over a bowl of Ready Brek and smile to oneself knowing that you surely have witnessed a miracle.

8   Telephone a stranger and ask to speak to their groin.

9   Put an end to father's quizzical looks by shaving off his eyebrows.

10   Get into the mind of Jack the Ripper by crouching in a darkened East End alleyway with a stethoscope in your carrier bag.

11 Make a tiny black phallus using the scrapings from
    some burnt toast.

12 Dust all your correspondence with iron filings to see if
    there are any hidden magnets amongst the documents.

13 Place starched white linen handkerchiefs over dog dirt in
    the street to make the streets appear slightly cleaner.

14 Make your own Branston Pickle by painting some dice
    brown and dropping them into a jar of three-in-one oil.

time break

15 Interrupt your sunday dinner Jarvis-Cocker-style by
    bursting into the dining-room and pushing over your two
    youngest siblings before strenuously denying said
    incident when seated subsequently at the dinner table.

16 Shout out 'It's parky Parky' whenever you see Michael
    Parkinson in cold weather.

17 Weedle out the chaff from the wood with a chaff
    weedler.

18 Recreate the horror of the Blitz by eating a winkle
    under two tons of rubble.

19 Confuse pensioners by putting a poster on your
    gatepost advertizing a jumble sale.

20 Re-baptize yourself, using cider and onions.

Dove from Above

Again, each player takes a turn at being the question master and the play moves to the left. The question master asks the player on their left to choose a number between 1 and 211 to select a question. This player receives two points for a correct answer. If another player feels they know the answer, then they must commence cooing like a dove. The first player to coo has the first chance to answer in event of a pass or an incorrect answer, the second player to coo has the second chance, and so on. If a player interrupts without cooing, one point is deducted from their score.

1 **Haircuts** What is the length of the average fringe? *Two inches.*

2 **Archaeology** Name three ancient civilizations. *Incas, Egyptians, Ridge People.*

3 **Cows** Name five breeds of cow in ten seconds.

4 **Cereals** Name five types of cereal in ten seconds.

5 **Mice** Who created Jerry? *Fred Quimby.*

6 **Shrubs** Name a personality with facial shrubbery. *Gaz Coombes.*

7 **Europe** Name five European capitals in ten seconds.

8 **Ten Commandments** What does covet mean? *It's a place where a fox lives.*

9 **Helicopters** Fergie has a little chopper called what? *Budgie.*

10 **Motorbikes** Name five makes of motorbike in ten seconds.

11 **Hot air ballooning** Richard Branson is not only a balloonist but he takes his name from a brand of pickle. Name three ingredients in Branston Pickle.

12 **Ladders** Name three types of ladder. *Step, rope, Jacob's.*

13 **Piggy wigs** What is crackling? *The crisp, brown skin of roast pork.*

14 **Cheese** Name five types of cheese in ten seconds.

15 **Tart foods** What is it that makes some foods tart? *Citric acid.*

16 **The Past** Give the dates of World War I. *1914 to 1918.*

17 **Biscuits** Name five types of biscuit in ten seconds.

18 **Spoons** Name a celebrity born with a silver spoon in their mouth. Then get a spoon and do an impression. *Pete Townshend.*

19 **Air travel** Name five modes of air travel in ten seconds.

20 **Pirates** You have ten seconds to rob another player.

21 **Dogs** Name a hairy dog. *Poodle*

22 **Fungus** Who traditionally hides under a toadstool. *A pixie.*

23 **Holidays** Name five public holidays in ten seconds.

24 **Drummers** Ginger Baker played drums for Cream. Name two other gingers. *Ginger Rogers, Ginger Tom.*

25 **Hitler** Name three people with Hitler moustaches. *Oliver Hardy, Ben Turpin, Hitler, Charlie Chaplin, Sparks.*

26 **Hats** Name five types of hat in ten seconds.

27 **Cooks** Reveal a Roger Cook-type exposé on another player and hound them for the next minute.

28 **Mammals** Name five mammals in ten seconds.

29 **Toiletries** To the nearest ten, how many pieces of toilet paper are there on a standard roll of high quality Kleenex? *44.*

30 **Money** Whose got the most cash on them? *The winner gains one point.*

31 **Berries** Leave the room and re-enter presenting your version of Chuck Berry's duck walk.

32 **Fabrics** Name five types of fabric in ten seconds.

33 **Bones** Where in your body is your paella? *In your stomach. It's a revolting Spanish rice dish.*

34 **Legs** When Rod Stewart wrote 'Hot Legs' was he referring to:

a) an experience with Deep Heat following a strenuous football match;

b) an incident related to him by a fireman who had to remove a burning table with Queen Anne legs from a hospice;

c) the feeling he experienced whilst on holiday in Spain sunbathing with only his legs exposed, the rest of his body still being in the van. *The answer is c.*

35 **Cakes** Name five types of cake in ten seconds.

36 **Jewellery** How many gold chains did Mr T wear? *Three hundred.*

37 **Breads** Name five types of bread in ten seconds.

38 **Soft furnishings** Give three different names for a sofa. *Settee, sofa, couch.*

39 **Light bulbs** Name a personality with a light bulb figure. *Arnold Schwarzenegger or Sandy Toksvig, depending on which way you look at it.*

40 **Chocolate** Name five chocolate bars in ten seconds.

41 **Dogs** Name a hairy dog. *Terrier.*

42 **Jockeys** Name a monkey that rides a horse. *Davey Jones.*

43 **Woollies** Name five styles of sweater in ten seconds.

44 **Precious stones** Name three celebrities named after precious stones. *Anne Diamond, Ruby Wax, Crystal Gayle, Billy Crystal, Joan Jet.*

45 **Golf** Name five golfers in ten seconds.

46 **Gingers** Name a pre-war ginger. *Ginger Rogers, Algernon Swinburn.*

47 **Nuts** Name five types of nut in ten seconds.

48 **The Rolling Stones** How many face lines does Keith Richards have? *Approximately 128.*

49 **Heaven** Showaddywaddy sang about the 'Three Steps to Heaven', but how many steps are there up the Eiffel Tower? *Two thousand.*

50 **Flowers** Name five types of flower in ten seconds.

51 **Cars** Name five types of car in ten seconds.

52 **Washing powder** Name five brands of washing powder in ten seconds.

53 **Metals** Name five types of metal in ten seconds.

54 **Gems** Name five types of gemstone in ten seconds.

55 **Jelly fish** Name another type of jelly-based animal. *Sea cucumber, sea mouse.*

56 **Tube** Name five tube lines in ten seconds.

57 **Old professions** What did a wainwright do? *He made carts.*

58 **Insects** Name five insects in ten seconds.

59 **Tramps** How old is Joan Collins? *67.*

60 **Nursery rhymes** Name five nusery rhymes in ten seconds.

61 **Cartoons** Name five cartoon characters in ten seconds.

62 **Dogs** Name a hairy dog. *Alsatian.*

63 **Head** Name five parts of the head in ten seconds.

64 **Organs** Name five organs of the human body in ten seconds.

65 **Mods 'n' Rockers** Name a famous mod or rocker.

66 **Cartoons** Name a pop star named after a cartoon. *Snoop Doggy Dog, Shaggy, Tom Petty.*

67 **Shoes** Name five types of shoe in ten seconds.

68 **Blondes** Blondie's singer was Debbie Harry, Prince Harry is the son of blonde Princess Diana. Yet Diana Ross has black hair. Discuss.

69 **Footballers** Name five footballers in ten seconds.

70 **Blue Peter** Name five *Blue Peter* presenters in ten seconds.

71 **Breweries** What is brewer's yeast taken as a preventive measure against? *Weakness.*

72 **Crisps** Name five flavours of crisps in ten seconds.

73 **Tudor period** How many slots, on average, did Henry VIII have in his doublets? *16.*

74 **Landmarks** Name five London landmarks in ten seconds.

75 **Fast food** Name five fast-food restaurant chains in ten seconds.

76 **Dogs** Name a hairy dog. *Labrador.*

77 **Games** True or false: dominoes was originally played in Italy using a kind of giant ladybird. *False.*

78 **Harnesses** Name a celebrity whose name sounds a bit like 'harness'. *Desi Arnes, Jessy Arness.*

79 **Muppets** Name five Muppets in ten seconds.

80 **Jewellery** Name five types of jewellery in ten seconds.

81 **Doilies** Name three leaders of the New Romantic movement. *Steve Strange, Boy George, Philip Salon.*

82 **Weather** Name five types of weather condition in ten seconds.

83 **Scotland** Name five places in Scotland in ten seconds.

84 **Crab movement** Leave the room and return with your version of a crab walking towards the sea and feeding at the same time. *Other players must remain stony-faced or lose a point.*

85 **Supermodels** Name five supermodels in ten seconds.

86 **Wine** Make a whining noise for one minute.

87 **Birds** Name five types of bird in ten seconds.

88 **Dogs** Name five breeds of dog in ten seconds.

89 **Wolves** Name a pop group from Wolverhampton. *Slade.*

90 **Wigs** Who is the odd man out: Terry Wogan, Burt Reynolds, Tina Turner, Tom Cruise. *No one, they all wear wigs. (No, it is Tom Cruise.)*

91 **Beer** Name five bitter brands in ten seconds.

92 **Trees** Name five celebrities named after trees. *Leslie Ash, Courtney Pine, Nigel Hawthorn, Alan Alda. Three extra points for Edward Woodward.*

93 *Dogs* Name a hairy dog. *Red Setter.*

94 **Chicken** Name a product with nothing to do with chicken or eggs, with a chicken on the packaging. *Cornflakes.*

95 **The Blues** Name five songs with 'blue' in the title in ten seconds.

96 **Joinery** Name five joinery tools in ten seconds.

97 **Buildings** If you laid the Empire State Building on its side, would people still bother using the lift? *No.*

98 **Lips** Give five words beginning with 'lip' in ten seconds, e.g. lipstick.

99 **Papers** Name five national newspapers in ten seconds.

100 **Birds** Name three celebrities named after birds. *Alan Partridge, Anthony Quayle, Eddie the Eagle, Annie Nightingale, Christopher Wren.*

101 **Butter** Name five brands of butter or margarine in ten seconds.

102 **Chips** You have 20 seconds to get some frozen chips and arrange them to spell 'BOOBS'.

103 **Fruits** Name five types of fruit in ten seconds.

104 **Eggs** Name five ways to cook an egg in ten seconds.

105 **Glue** You have 30 seconds to give an amusing true anecdote involving glue. If the other players decide you made it up, you lose one point.

106 **Trees** Name five types of tree in ten seconds.

107 **Building sites** What must be worn when walking round a building site? *Clothes.*

108 **Tea** name five types of tea in ten seconds.

109 **Meat** Name three celebrities named after types of meat. *Francis Bacon, Alan Lamb, Berry Venison.*

110 **Judges** From what hair is a judge's wig made? *The hair of hung criminals.*

111 **Fish** Name three celebrities named after fish. *Richard Herring, Magnus Pike, Alfie Bass, Ken Loach, Jackson Pollack. (No points for James Whale, two points for Fish from Marillion.*

112 **Supermarket** Name five high-street supermarkets in ten seconds.

113 **Dogs** Name a hairy dog. *Golden Retriever.*

114 **The Rich** How much is ex-Take That singer, Gary Barlow, worth? *Sixteen million pounds.*

115 **Fizzy drinks** Name five fizzy drinks in ten seconds.

116 **Banks** Name five high-street banks in ten seconds.

117 **Mars** Is it possible to cover both of one's eyes with one Mars bar. *Yes.*

118 **Americans** Name five Americans in ten seconds.

119 **Randy tom cats** Name one of Steve Coogan's fancy women. *Anna, Katrina.*

120 **Puffs** What was Jonathan Ross's first TV show called? *The Last Resort.*

121 **Doctors** Name five TV doctors in ten seconds. *Dr Kildare, Dr Who, Doctor in the House, Dr Mike, Dr Ruth.*

122 **Countries** Name three celebrities named after countries. *Jools Holland, Jill Ireland, Mike England.*

123 **Trees** Name five products that have a tree on their packaging. *Ye Olde Ham, Izal, any Spar product.*

124 **Sauce** Name five ingredients of ketchup. *Vinegar, tomatoes, sugar, salt, spices.*

125 **Soups** Who had an LP called *Goat's Head Soup?* *The Rolling Stones.*

126 **Eggs** Give an anecdote of a time when you misheard someone and thought they said 'fried egg' instead of 'Friday'.

127 **Doctor Who** Name five actors who have played Doctor Who in ten seconds.

128 **Colours** Name three celebrities with a colour in their name. *Barry White, James Brown, Black, Peter Green, Barry Blue, Red Adaire.*

129 **Panties** Name five slang words for ladies' underpants. *Scanties, bloomers, drawers, knickers, unmentionables.*

130 **Candy** What do Americans call candy floss? *Cotton candy.*

131 **Dogs** Name a hairy dog. *Afghan.*

132 **Monkeys** Name a cheeky TV monkey. *Cheetah, Topov.*

133 **Banks** Name five banks in ten seconds.

134 **Fruit** Name three celebrities named after fruit. *Jason Orange, Jack Lemmon, Neneh Cherry.*

135 **Soup** Name five soups in ten seconds.

136 **Letters** APAT_CLVLSSC: what is the missing letter? *'G' for Gemini.*

137 **Ices** Name five ice-cream flavours in ten seconds.

138 **Pythons** Name five members of the Monty Python team. *Palin, Idle, Chapman, Gilliam, Jones, Cleese.*

139 **Chips** How many chips, to the nearest one, could you get into an empty bag which measures eight inches by four inches? *One. After that it isn't an empty bag.*

140 **Years** How many years in a decade have 364 days? *Ten. They all have at least 364.*

141 **Briefs** Name five pop stars known by one name only in ten seconds. *Sting, Madonna, Prince, Elvis, Seal.*

142 **Bars** Name five things found on a pub bar in ten seconds.

143 **Noise** What is the loudest noise you can make easily in the kitchen? *Throwing the oven out of the window.*

144 **Sight** How far can the unaided human eye see? *Forever.*

145 **Doors** Name five parts of a door in ten seconds.

146 **Dogs** Name a hairy dog. *Springer Spaniel.*

147 **Bivalves** Which other bivalves have the oysters been at war with since the beginning of time? *The clams.*

148 **France** Incorporate these words to make a sentence in French: pantalon, garçon, brun, cheval, la peanu.

149 **Bras** Name a woman generally considered to be a 'bra buster'.

150 **Cups** Name five sporting cups in ten seconds.

151 **China** Does bone china contain bones? *Yes.*

152 **Dogs** Name a hairy dog. *Husky.*

153 **Coats** Name three celebrities with types of coat in their names. *Geoff Capes, Cecil Parker, Cameron Macintosh.*

154 **Ink** Give five words ending in 'ink' in ten seconds.

155 **Fire** Represent fire through the medium of dance.

156 **Ice** Visualize and present a piece of modern dance that represents the Terror of Ice.

157 **Fingers** Which one of Henry VIII's wives had six fingers? *Anne Boleyn.*

158 **Ice** When Ice T refers to a 'bitch in the hood', is he talking about:

a) A dog under the bonnet of his bonnet;

b) An unpleasant woman in the hood of his parka;

c) A big itch under the hood of his penis.

None, he refers to a visit by Joan Collins to HMS Hood during a World War II Pacific campaign.

159 **Parts of the body** Name three personalities who take their name from parts of the body. *Michael Foot, Tony Head, Dr Legg, Tom Thumb. (Four points for Tony Hancock.)*

160 **Fish** Name five fish in ten seconds.

161 **Hell** You must say 'bloody hell' within the next five minutes. *If it is spotted by another player you will lose two points; if not, you gain two points.*

162 **Veal** What is veal? *A delicious, tender meat.*

163 **Camping** What was the biggest-selling colour for tents in the UK in 1994? *Blue.*

164 **Seconds** How many seconds in 32 years? *Billion.*

165 **Cooking** Name five kitchen implements in ten seconds.

166 **Veins** How many miles of veins and arteries do people have? *Fifty-five thousand miles.*

167 **Cooks** Name five chefs in ten seconds.

168 **Metals** Name three celebrities named after metals. *Freddie Mercury, Jeremy Irons, David Steel.*

169 **Citrus fruit** Name five types of citrus fruit in ten seconds.

170 **Beans** How much does a standard can of beans weigh? *420 grams.*

171 **Spuds** What item of clothing is Marks & Spencer's biggest seller? *Men's underpants.*

172 **Etiquette** On a wedding night who should use the toilet first? *Whoever is most desperate for a shit.*

173 **Fights** Who is the best fighter: Lee Evans or Jack Dee? *Lee Evans.*

174 **Female singers** Name five female singers in ten seconds.

175 **Royalty** Name all four members of the group Queen. *Mercury, Taylor, May, Deacon.*

176 **Dogs** Name a hairy dog. *Old English Sheepdog.*

177 **Bodies** What part of the body is at its gravitational centre when you lie down with your arms by your side. *The right ventricle of the heart.*

178 **Transport** Name five modes of transport in ten seconds.

179 **Missing person** What are the three missing letters: JAS, MAR, HOW, GAR? *ROB.*

180 **Politicians** Name five politicians in ten seconds.

181 **Places** Name three celebrities named after English towns. *Tony Blackburn, Rod Hull, Dionne Warwick, Sarah Lancaster, Burt Lancaster, Jack London.*

182 **Reindeer** Which country consumes the largest amount of reindeer meat? Sweden.

183 **Butter** What are the ingredients of peanut butter? *Peanuts.*

184 **Cutlery** Name five pieces of cutlery in ten seconds.

185 **Crisps** What is the maximum number of crisps, to the nearest ten, obtained from a single potato? *172.*

186 **Bacon** What is the average meat-to-fat ratio, to the nearest five per cent, on a standard rasher of streaky bacon? *62 per cent meat to 38 per cent fat.*

187 **Sauces** Name five sauces in ten seconds.

188 **Geographical features** Name three celebrities who take their names from geographical features. *Jimmy Hill. (Two extra points for Billy Two Rivers.)*

189 **Actress** Name five actresses in ten seconds.

190 **Cheeses** What is the diameter of the largest recorded hole in a block of Emmenthal? *Seven centimetres.*

191 **Dogs** Name a hairy dog. *King Charles Spaniel.*

192 **Coconuts** The coconut is a hairy nut, can you name another hairy nut? *Cob nut.*

193 **Authors** Name five authors in ten seconds.

194 **Brides** Who is Desmond Wilcox's showbiz bride? *Esther Rantzen.*

195 **Occupations** Name three celebrities with an occupation as their last name. *Richard Baker, Pat Butcher, Francis Farmer, Shaw Taylor, Henry Cooper, Christopher Plumber.*

196 **Painters** Name five painters in ten seconds.

197 **Letters** Who was the singer in ABC? *Martin Fry.*

198 **Bottles** What are the two constituents of glass? *Sand and blood.*

199 **Pails and buckets** My pail holds two gallons but has a hole in it. My bucket holds one gallon and is completely watertight. Which should I take on holiday with me? *Neither, take a suitcase, love.*

200 **Sportswomen** Name five sportswomen in ten seconds.

201 **Feet** To the nearest foot, how long is a tiger's tail. *3 foot.*

202 **Wheels** You have 30 seconds to find out the number of the local meals-on-wheels service.

203 **Rats** Name a celebrity love-rat.

204 **Sportsmen** Name five sportsmen in ten seconds.

205 **Peanuts** Name a personality whose initials are K.P. *Keith Prowse, Kieran Prendergast, Kerry Packer.*

206 **Trumpets** Name three trumpeters.

207 **Birds** Each player must give a girl's first name, following the alphabet (eg. player 1: Anita, player 2: Betty, etc) *If a player hesitates or fails they are out. When 'z' is reached return to A and so on until no players are left. The last one left is awarded two points.*

208 **Porn** Strike a reader's wife-style pose and remain in said pose for 20 seconds, in silence. *If during the pose any player makes a noise they lose a point.*

209 **Loch Ness** Leave the room and come back, in silence, adopting the appearance of Nessy. *If anyone makes a noise during the ten-second performance, one point will be deducted from the culprit.*

210 **Actors** Name five actors in ten seconds.

211 **Animals** Name three celebrities with animals in their names. *Virginia Woolf, Alan Lamb, Dusty Hare, Sam Fox, Adrian Mole, Seal, Snoop Doggy Dog.*

212 **The Jacksons** Name two Jacksons. *Michael, Marlon, Gordon.*

213 **Sherbet dips** Give a personal anecdote about a sherbet dip. *The other players should decide whether it is worth a point or not.*

214 **Calendars** You have 15 seconds to bring a calendar to the other players.

215 **Cornflakes** Who invented cornflakes? *Kelloggs.*

216 **Eagles.** Name the two astronaut who landed on the moon in The Eagle. *Aldrin and Armstrong.*

217 **Boils** You have 10 seconds to give four words that rhyme with 'boils'.

218 **The Moon** Do the moonwalk.

219 **Male singers** Name five male singers in ten seconds.

220 **Toilet paper** You have 15 seconds to return to the other players with a toilet roll. *Ten extra points if it is attached to a baby Labrador.*

221 **Dogs** Name a hairy dog. *Border Collie.*

Quick Fire

Begin this round by playing track 49 of the *Shooting Stars* CD. Each player asks three questions randomly selected from the Quick Fire section. If there are three or more players then the first player to shout 'Ulrikakaka' gets the first chance to answer, the second player to shout 'Ulrikakaka' gets the second chance, and so on. A player receives two points for a correct answer and loses two points for an incorrect answer.

1 Which member of Bananarama went on to form the group Shakespear's Sister? *Siobhan Fahey.*

2 Which comedian starred as Jolson in the West End musical? *Brian Conley.*

3 Which English footballer scored the first goal of the Euro96 competition? *Alan Shearer.*

4 Who plays Gary's girlfriend, Dorothy, in the comedy *Men Behaving Badly*? *Caroline Quentin.*

5 Marti Pellow is the lead singer of which group? *Wet Wet Wet.*

6 Who played Arthur Daley in Minder? *George Cole.*

7 Whitney Houston had a huge number one hit from the film *The Bodyguard*. What was it called? *I Will Always Love You.*

8 Who plays Pauline Fowler in EastEnders? *Wendy Richards.*

9 Which particularly unusual ability do the cast members of the stage musical *Starlight Express* have? *Rollerskating.*

10 Who is the host of the revamped Saturday Live comedy show? *Lee Hurst.*

11 Which pop-star brothers played *The Krays* on the big screen? *Gary and Martin Kemp.*

12 Alma tries to avoid Stephen, but how will she feel when Deirdre hits it off with the handsome Canadian? From which soap opera would you expect to find this storyline? *Coronation Street.*

13 In the Dustin Hoffman film *Outbreak*, which animal was responsible for the spread of the killer virus? *A monkey.*

14 Actor Jack Shepherd plays which Cornish detective? *Wycliffe.*

15 On which quiz show might you ask Bob for a 'P'? *Blockbusters.*

16 Who is the host of *It Will be Alright on the Night*? *Dennis Norden*

17 *Frontiers* star, Peter Howitt, also starred in *Bread* as which of the Boswells? *Joey.*

18 In *Dad's Army*, what is the daytime job of Private Fraser? *Undertaker.*

19 Which two characters in *Friends* are brother and sister? *Monica and Ross.*

20 Which actor made Demi Moore an indecent proposal in the film of the same name? *Robert Redford.*

21 In which series might you find Ma and Pa Larkin? *The Darling Buds of May.*

22 Tom Jones had a hit with a cover version of which Prince song? *'Kiss'.*

23 Agnetha, Fridja and Bjorn were three members of Abba. Who was the fourth? *Benny.*

24 Who took 'a small step for a man, a giant leap for mankind in 1969?' *Neil Armstrong*

25 Who is the host of the TV quiz *Midas Touch*? *Bradley Walsh*

26 Who stars as Jack Frost in *A Touch of Frost*? *David Jason.*

27 Richard and Judy began their evening chat show by interviewing which controversial celebrity figure? *O.J. Simpson.*

28 In which comedy series would you find the characters Hawkeye, Klinger and Radar O'Reilly? *M*A*S*H**.

29 Which actor plays Wayne in the comedy drama series *Bad Boys*? *Karl Howman.*

30 In which soap would you find the Tate family? *Emmerdale.*

31 Which comedienne stars in *Murder Most Horrid*? *Dawn French.*

32 Which comedienne has the alter ego Gayle Tuesday? *Brenda Gilhooly.*

33 Bryan Adams had a number one hit with the theme from the film *Robin Hood: Prince of Thieves*. What was it called? *'Everything I do I do for You'.*

34 Moxey, Oz and Wayne were characters in which hit comedy drama series? *Auf Wiedersehn Pet.*

35 Sarah Cox is a presenter on which late night programme? *The Girlie Show.*

36 Which was the better looking, Beauty or the Beast? *Beauty.*

37 Andy Bell and Vince Clark are members of which group? *Erasure.*

38 Which children's TV presenter replaced Jason Donovan in the lead role of the musical *Joseph and the Amazing Technicolour Dreamcoat*? *Phillip Schofield.*

39 Which pop star appeared regularly in the soap *Hollyoaks*? *Alvin Stardust.*

40 Who starred opposite Jamie Lee Curtis in the action movie *True Lies*? *Arnold Schwarzenegger.*

41 Which frenetic British comedian starred in the film *Funny Bones*? *Lee Evans.*

42 In which country was the flop soap *Eldorado* set? *Spain.*

43 Which of the McGann brothers has played the role of Doctor Who? *Paul.*

44 Who left the pop group Eternal to go solo? *Louise.*

45 Pop star Phil Collins is the drummer with which group? *Genesis.*

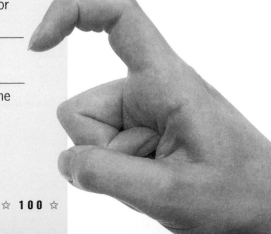

46 Babylon Zoo had a hit song which was used in a jeans commercial. What was it called? *'Spaceman'*.

47 Which controversial tennis player screamed, 'You cannot be serious!'? *John McEnroe*.

48 Name the rap star who is also a presenter on *Baadasss TV?* *Ice T*.

49 In *Jack and Jeremy's Real Lives*, Jack is Jack Dee. Which comedian is Jeremy? *Jeremy Hardy*.

50 Who is the host of the TV quiz *Today's The Day?* *Martyn Lewis*.

51 Actor Tom Cruise starred in the film version of which sixties adventure series? *Mission Impossible*.

52 Who had a hit single with the song 'Material Girl'? *Madonna*.

53 Who narrates *Thomas the Tank Engine* on television? *Ringo Starr*.

54 What does Paul McKenna do to people on his television show? *Hypnotizes them*.

55 Who released an album entitled *Different Class?* *Pulp*.

56 Which animal would you associate with Rod Hull? *Emu*.

57 Stonefish is a character in which Australian soap? *Neighbours*.

58 What's the name of Postman Pat's black and white cat? *Jess*.

59 James Bolam played Terry in *The Likely Lads*. Who played Bob? *Rodney Bewes*.

60 Which Gladiator presents the TV show *You Bet* with Darren Day? *Jet*.

61 Who presents the TV quiz show *Backdate?* *Valerie Singleton*.

62 Who wrote the best-selling book *A Brief History of Time?* *Professor Stephen Hawking*.

63 Who likes to show off his *Auntie's Bloomers* on TV? *Terry Wogan*.

64 John Thaw and Dennis Waterman starred in which seventies detective series? *The Sweeney*.

65 The Pet Shop Boys recorded the theme tune to which TV fashion show? *The Clothes Show*.

66 Who appears on TV *Live and Uncut?* *Richard Littlejohn*.

67 Ambridge is the setting for which long-running radio programme? *The Archers.*

68 Robert Smith is the lead singer of which group? *The Cure.*

69 Pippa's dad Bert and his friend Harry turn up and decide that trouble is looming. From which soap would you expect to find this storyline? *Home and Away.*

70 What is the name of Tintin's dog? *Snowy.*

71 What is the name of Charlie Brown's dog in the *Peanuts* cartoons? *Snoopy.*

72 Timon and Zazu are characters in which Disney cartoon feature? *The Lion King.*

73 In the movie *Forrest Gump*, which rock' n' roll star did young Forrest teach how to dance? *Elvis Presley.*

74 Who wrote the rock opera *Tommy*? *Pete Townsend.*

75 Which country does pop star Björk come from? *Iceland.*

76 In the movie *Batman Forever*, which actor played The Riddler? *Jim Carrey.*

77 Who is the presenter of *Home Front*? *Tessa Shaw.*

78 Who is the female presenter of *The Really Wild Show*? *Michaela Strachan.*

79 Who is the director of the award-winning movie *Secrets and Lies*? *Mike Leigh.*

80 In which family is the daughter called Wednesday? *The Addams Family.*

81 Who is the co-host of *Sport in Question* with Jimmy Greaves? *Ian St. John.*

82 Who created the character of Budgie the Little Helicopter? *Sarah Ferguson.*

83 Which group released an album entitled *Bizarre Fruit*? *M People.*

84 Who is the presenter of *The Time...the Place*? *John Stapleton.*

85 In which London Street did Sherlock Homes live? *Baker Street.*

86 Which detective series features the characters John Munch and Steve Crosetti? *Homicide: Life on the Street.*

88 Which actor played Withnail in the movie *Withnail and I*? *Richard E. Grant.*

89 Which millionaire businessman owns his own airline but prefers to travel by hot air balloon? *Richard Branson.*

90 Patrick Robinson plays which character in *Casualty*? *Ash.*

91 What was the name of the character played by Frances de la Tour in the classic comedy series *Rising Damp*? *Miss Jones.*

92 What was unusual about the character of Rimmer in *Red Dwarf*? *He was a hologram.*

93 The Corkhill family feature in which TV soap? *Brookside.*

94 Who is the host of the quiz show *Crosswit*? *Tom O'Connor.*

95 PC Reg Hollis goes undercover, plunging him into a seedy world of vice. From which TV series would you expect to find this storyline? *The Bill.*

96 Which band did John Lydon form after leaving the Sex Pistols? *PiL.*

97 Which former music-hall star sang the theme music to *Dad's Army*? *Bud Flannagan.*

98 Which comedian called Prince Charles a 'grovelling little bastard'? *Spike Milligan.*

99 Stingray, Captain Scarlet and Thunderbirds were all puppet series created by whom? *Jerry Anderson.*

100 Who played Rebecca in the sitcom *Cheers*? *Kirstey Alley.*

101 Which actor had to tell his wife *Honey, I Shrunk the Kids*? *Rick Moranis.*

102 Name the actor who talked to the trees? *Clint Eastwood.*

103 Benny the Ball, Choo-Choo and Brains were members of whose gang? *Top Cat's.*

104 Which controversial artist exhibited a dead sheep in formaldehyde? *Damien Hirst.*

105 Who is TV weather girl Suzanne Charlton's famous dad? *Bobby Charlton.*

106 Which movie starred Nicholas Cage and Brigit Fonda as lottery winners? *It Could Happen to You.*

107 Which Harry is Frank Bruno referring to when he says, 'know what I mean 'arry'? *Harry Carpenter.*

108 Which actress starred in the movies *The Specialist, The Quick and the Dead* and *Casino*? *Sharon Stone.*

109 EastEnders actors Susan Tully and Todd Carty started out in which children's TV series? *Grange Hill.*

110 Who is the billionaire owner of Microsoft? *Bill Gates.*

111 Who is the object of Compo's affections in the comedy series *Last of the Summer Wine*? *Nora Batty.*

112 Who is the director of the films *She's Gotta Have It, Do the Right Thing* and *Girl 6*? *Spike Lee.*

113 Which comedian made a *World Tour of Scotland*? *Billy Connolly.*

114 Name the illusionist who apparently walked through the Great Wall of China. *David Copperfield.*

115 What was the name of the comedy show that launched the careers of Rowan Atkinson, Smith, Griff Rhys Jones and Pamela Stephenson? *Not the 9 O'Clock News.*

116 Which actor played the role of Rumpole of the Bailey? *Leo McKern.*

117 Which movie contains a scene in which actress Meg Ryan fakes an orgasm in a restaurant? *When Harry Met Sally.*

118 Name the tennis star who was stabbed in the back during a match by a crazed fan of her main rival? *Monica Seles.*

119 Who is the quiz master of the nineties version of *University Challenge*? *Jeremy Paxman.*

120 Which actor plays Dr Finlay in the TV series of the same name? *Ian Bannen.*

121 Which politician's son became lost in the desert? *Margaret Thatcher's.*

122 Who would often complain, 'That's another fine mess you've got me into'? *Oliver Hardy.*

123 Which comedian would you associate with the catch phrase 'Just like that'? *Tommy Cooper.*

124 The Fugees had a number one hit with 'Killing me Softly'. Who sang the original version? *Roberta Flak.*

125 Which actress starred in the movies *Mask, Mermaids* and *The Witches of Eastwick*? *Cher.*

126 On which TV programme does Michael Aspel surprise celebrities with a big red book? *This is Your Life.*

127 In the film *Carry on Cleo,* which actor cries 'Infamy, Infamy, they've all got it in for me'? *Kenneth Williams.*

128 Which actress played Marianne in Emma Thompson's film, *Sense and Sensibility? Kate Winslett.*

129 Which pop star was *The Man Who Fell To Earth? David Bowie.*

130 Homer, Marge and Bart are members of which TV family? *The Simpsons.*

131 Which long-running children's TV programme would you associate with sticky-back plastic? *Blue Peter.*

132 In which city does Batman live? *Gotham.*

133 Which actress caused a stir when she appeared naked and pregnant on the front cover of the magazine *Vanity Fair? Demi Moore.*

134 Which actor starred in the movies *The Colour of Money, Butch Cassidy and the Sundance Kid* and *Cool Hand Luke? Paul Newman.*

135 Which actor starred in the movies *Tootsie, Rainman* and *The Graduate? Dustin Hoffman.*

136 Who played Frank Spencer in *Some Mothers Do Have 'em? Michael Crawford.*

137 Name the star of *London's Burning* who released a debut single called 'Only You'? *John Alford.*

138 In whose TV show would you find a baby called Frogmella? *Harry Enfield's.*

139 Which actor is famous for his role as Jim Rockford in *The Rockford Files? James Garner.*

140 Which actor starred in the movies *Witness, Bladerunner* and *The Fugitive? Harrison Ford.*

141 In which programme does Statto appear? *Fantasy Football League.*

142 Name the third film in the *Star Wars* trilogy. *Return of the Jedi.*

143 'Ain't no Doubt' was a number one hit in 1992 for which Geordie actor? *Jimmy Nail.*

144 Which of the Marks Brothers played the harp? *Harpo.*

145 Who hosts the weekend show with the help of Daley Thompson & Lisa Tarbuck? *Dale Winton.*

146 Who presented the *Good Sex Guide*? *Margi Clarke.*

147 Who replaced Steve Wright on the *Morning Show* on Radio 1? *Chris Evans.*

148 Which Prince song did Tom Jones have a hit with? *Kiss.*

149 Actor Phil Daniels featured in which Blur single? *Parklife.*

150 In which 1942 film does Bing Crosby sing 'White Christmas'? *Holiday Inn.*

151 Who plays Gordon Brittas in *The Brittas Empire*? *Chris Barrie.*

152 Who recently signed a modelling contract with *Estee Lauder*? *Liz Hurley.*

153 Top band Portishead come from which West country city? *Bristol.*

154 Name a comedy double act. *Morecambe & Wise, Hale & Pace, Little & Large.*

155 Who was the first actor to play Dr Who on television? *William Hartnell.*

156 What was the name of Dorothys' dog in *Wizard of Oz*? *Toto.*

157 In the comedy film what was the Pink Panther? *A diamond.*

158 Who plays TV's Inspector Colombo? *Peter Falk.*

159 Who is Rupert the Bear's Badger friend? *Bill.*

160 The Dingles family feature in which TV soap? *Emmerdale.*

161 Susan Brookes is the resident chef on what programme? *This Morning.*

162 Anton Rodgers plays a solicitor who marries a younger woman in which series? *May to December.*

163 Who is the host of *Stars in Their Eyes*? *Matthew Kelly.*

164 Who hosts TV's *Big Break*? *Jim Davidson.*

165 Which actor was buried in *Four Weddings and a Funeral*? *Simon Callow.*

166 How many times a week is *The Bill* broadcast? *Three.*

167 Who is the *Man from Auntie*? *Ben Elton.*

168 Who is better known as Guinness and Mead? *Little & Large.*

169 Who hosts *The Price is Right?*
Leslie Crowther.

170 Who directed the film *Bullets over Broadway?*
Woody Allen.

171 Which 1980's film starred John Hurt as John Merrick? *Elephant Man.*

172 What was the name of Rigsby's cat in *Rising Damp? Vienna.*

173 What is the name of Blackadder's sidekick? *Baldrick.*

174 Lesley Joseph plays which character in *Birds of a Feather?*
Dorian.

175 *Going Straight* was the sequel to which comedy series?
Porridge.

176 Which flowers are associated with Dame Edna Everage?
Gladioli.

177 Who did Neil Morrissey replace in *Men Behaving Badly?*
Harry Enfield.

178 What are the names of the two puppets featured regularly on Big Breakfast? *Zig & Zag.*

179 Which one of the Monkees always wore a bobble hat? *Mike Nesbit.*

180 Who is Jasper Carrott's partner in *The Detectives? Robert Powell.*

181 Who played the part of Holly Golightly in *Breakfast at Tiffany's? Audrey Hepburn.*

182 Who sang 'You're the one that I want' in the movie *Grease?*
John Travolta, Olivia Newton-John.

183 Who is Stuart Goddard better known as? *Adam Ant.*

184 Alex Winter and Keanu Reeves had excellent adventures as which two characters? *Bill & Ted.*

185 Who had a number one hit in 1971 with 'Seasons in the Sun'? *Terry Jacks.*

186 Which character is played by Sid Owen in *EastEnders?*
Ricky.

187 The film *Drop Dead Fred* starred which British comedian?
Rik Mayall.

188 Who played the elder daughter, Bobby, in the 1972 film *The Railway Children*? *Jenny Agutter.*

189 Which sport did Madonna play in the film *A League of their Own*? *Baseball.*

190 'Colonel Bogey' was the theme tune to which classic 1957 film? *Bridge on the River Kwai.*

191 Which film character has a valet called Cato? *Inspector Clousseau.*

192 What does the G stand for in the American film production company AGM? *Goldwyn.*

193 How many cooks compete in the show *Masterchef*? *Three.*

194 Who is the host of *Hotel Babylon*? *Dani Behr.*

195 What is the name of the hit seventies comedy series written by Carla Lane that has been resurrected for the nineties? *The Liver Birds.*

196 What are the names of the two rival gangs in the movie *West Side Story*? *The Sharks and the Jets.*

197 Who is the host of *That's Showbusiness*? *Mike Smith.*

198 In which Soap opera would you find brothers Phil and Grant Mitchell? *EastEnders.*

199 In which town do the Flintstones live? *Bedrock.*

200 Which character was played by Larry Hagman in *Dallas*? *JR.*

201 The detective series *Spender* is based in which city? *Newcastle.*

202 Which puppet would you associate with Matthew Corbett? *Sooty.*

203 What is the real name of the character Curly in *Coronation Street*? *Norman Watts.*

204 In which room might you find Nick Hancock? *Room 101.*

205 Who is the presenter of *The South Bank Show*? *Melvyn Bragg.*

206 What is the surname of Delboy and Rodney in *Only Fools and Horses*? *Trotter.*

207 What is the name of the police station in *The Bill*? *Sun Hill.*

208 Which actress plays the long-suffering wife of Victor Meldrew in *One Foot in the Grave*? *Annette Crosbie.*

209 In which English county is the drama series *Peak Practice* set? *Derbyshire.*

210 In *Emmerdale*, what is the name of the nearest town? *Hotten.*

211 Mrs Merton is the alter ego of which comedy actress? *Caroline Aherne.*

212 Whose 1996 album is entitled *Older*? *George Michael.*

213 What is the name of the secretary played by Jane Horrocks in *Absolutely Fabulous*? *Bubbles.*

214 Who is the mathematician on Channel 4's *Countdown*? *Carol Vorderman.*

215 In which bar would you find Norm and Cliff? *Cheers.*

216 Film director Terry Gilliam was once a member of which famous comedy team? *Monty Python's Flying Circus.*

217 Becky and Darlene are the daughters of which American comedy character? *Roseanne.*

218 Lex Luthor is the arch-enemy of which super-hero? *Superman.*

219 Who is the host of *Man o Man*? *Chris Tarrant.*

220 Which pop singer plays the son of *Dangerfield*? *Sean Maguire.*

221 What is the name of David Hasselhoff's character in *Baywatch*? *Mitch Buchanan.*

222 Who provided the voice for Woody in the animated film *Toy Story*? *Tom Hanks.*

223 Which group had a top 10 hit with the theme song from the comedy series *Friends*? *The Rembrandts.*

224 Who is the host of *Animal Hospital*? *Rolf Harris.*

225 Who is the oldest of the *Golden Girls*? *Sophia.*

226 Who starred as a death-row prisoner, opposite Susan Sarandon, in the film *Dead Man Walking*? *Sean Penn.*

227 Summer Bay is the setting for which soap opera? *Home and Away.*

Consolation

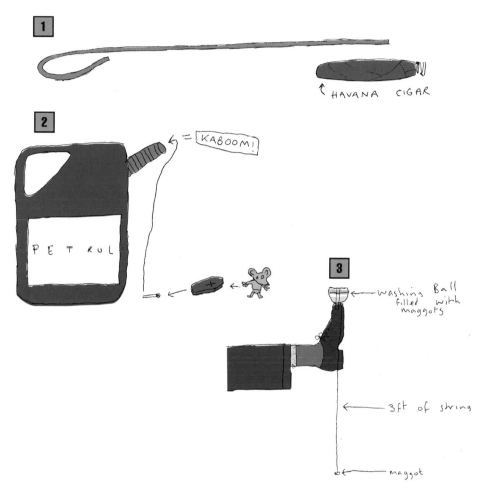

1   **The car cigar.** A unique device that allows you to introduce a
    Havana cigar deep into the workings of your car, via the exhaust.

2   **Mouse cremation kit.** Has your mouse passed away or
    perhaps you're just chanced across a dead mouse? Either way,
    no need for an expensive time-consuming funeral, simply
    cremate the mouse using the mouse cremation kit.
    Petrol and mouse in coffin + match = kaboom.
    No more mouse, sir!

3   **Coarse fishing shoe.** How often have you passed by a stream
    or river and realized that you've forgotten to put your rod and
    tackle in your wallet? No need to get vexed any more. Simply
    wear the coarse fishing shoe and watch the cod line up for your
    attention.

Prizes

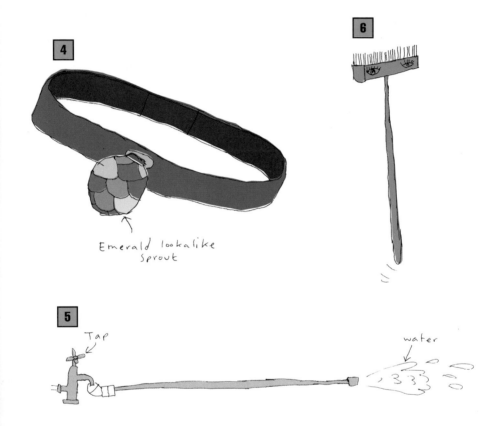

Emerald lookalike
sprout

Tap

water

4 **Sprout choker.** A beautiful emerald choker. But look closer, it's not an emerald but a rotting sprout. The ideal prize for a sworn enemy.

5 **Salt-people-invasion defence system.** It is becoming all too clear that at some stage the earth will be invaded by salt people. This defence system will foil their plans by turning them into brine. (It's a hose-pipe.)

6 **Mucky-book-purchasing robot.** Embarrassed to purchase your favourite mucky books? No worries, this broom robot will purchase them on your behalf and bring them to your bedside in his bristly fingers.

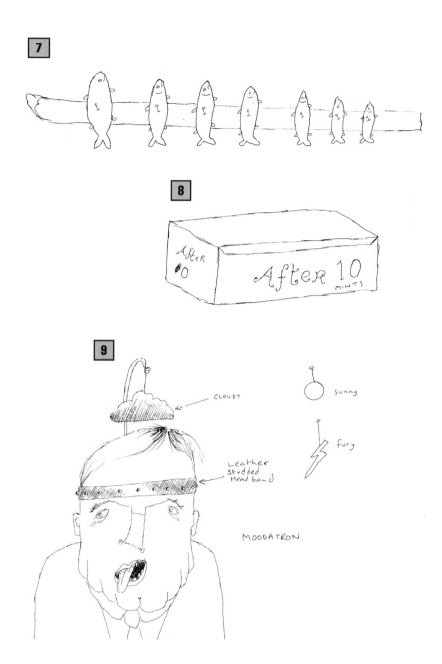

7   **Carpskichord.** Seven different-sized, hardened, ornamental carp banded on to a ski to make the most beautiful alpine sounds you have ever heard.

8   **After-ten mints.** If your dinner party goes on too long (eg. you start watching Tommy Vance's night-fly show), then simply bring out the after-ten mints.

9   **Moodatron.** Indicate to your workmates your present state of mind by hanging the appropriate symbol on your moodatron. Guaranteed to make your workplace less of an emotional battlefield.

QUOTES
P 51 - God rest ye merry gentlemen.
P 97 - Gawd 'elp us
P 112 - Holy Moses
P 264 - Hot Crossed bun story

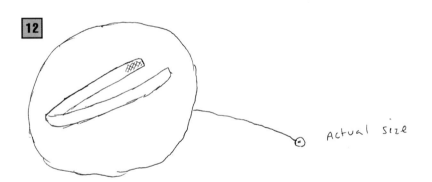

Actual size

10 **Vice Quad.** A four-wheel vehicle dedicated to ridding your town of pornography and prostitutes.

11 **Crispbread Bible.** The entire Bible printed on crispbread. Ideal for hungry Sunday school teachers.

12 **Wasp-dung tweezers.** Before you kill a wasp, remove its precious dung with these tweezers.

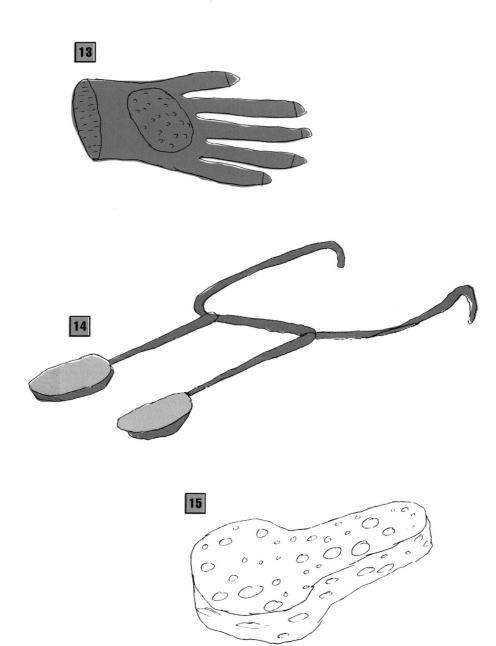

13 **Velcro prayer gloves.** Attach Velcro to palms of gloves to assist reluctant Christians.

14 **Eye spoons.** To collect your eyes should they pop out on your first visit to a nudist beach.

15 **Absorbent bicycle seat.**

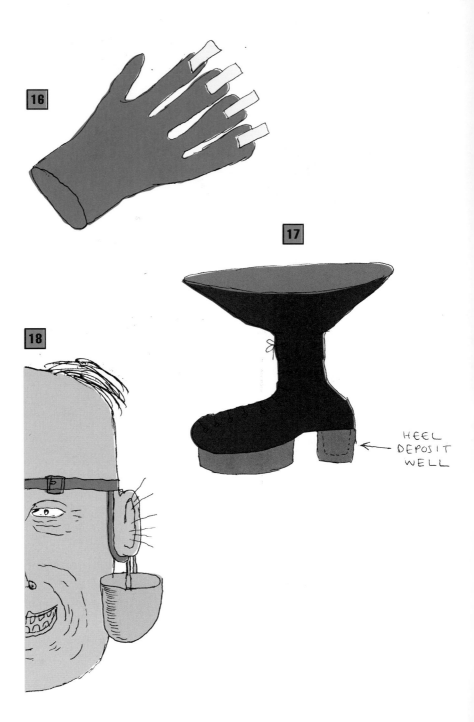

HEEL
DEPOSIT
WELL

16 Litmus gloves. To test the acidity of individual tapas dishes.

17 Tapas boot bucket. A shoe/bucket to catch tapas droppings. These are stored in the heel for future research into Spanish food.

18 Ear bags. Small canvas pouches that hang on each ear and collect hair and wax for use in tapas cookery.

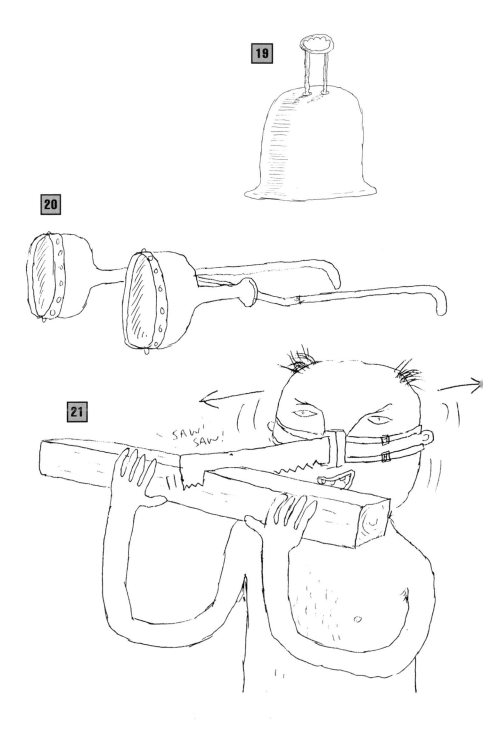

19 Tapas-growing bell. Simply place the bell over a saucer of dog food and scrape the tapas off the bell's surface one week later.

20 Infrared tapas spectacles. To see what you're actually eating in a dingy tapas bar.

21 Status Quo face saw. Saw away, as the music of the Quo makes your head nod to provide the thrust cut, leaving your hands free to practise air guitar.

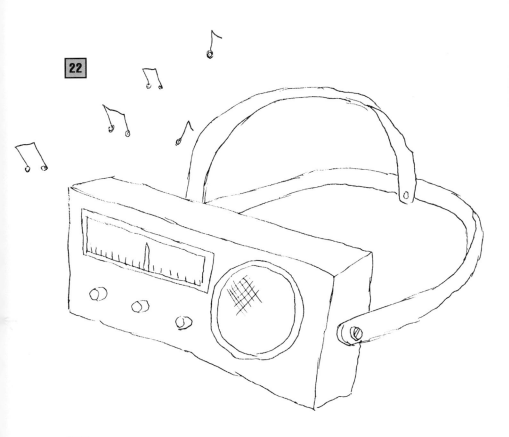

22 **Face radio.** A harness to attach your radio to your face
so you can listen to your favourite music whilst you're on
the move.

23 **Duncan balls.** Savoury dough balls with a 'D' on them,
which stick to your face for decoration or can be used as
a type of electric-free time machine.

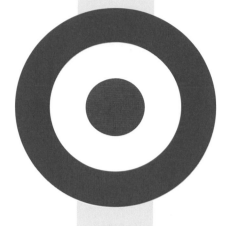

Punishments

1 Sweep the drive with a toothbrush.

2 Drink a can of creamed rice in one.

3 Wear a beard made from syrup and tea leaves.

4 Wear the clothes of the the smallest person in the house for one hour.

5 Clean the largest window in the house with a cottonbud.

6 Make a morbid sound from inside the airing cupboard for 30 minutes.

7 Get underneath the sofa and remain there for 15 minutes.

8 Tape a broom to your back and wander up and down the street shouting, 'I am the broom from the moon.'

9 Dig a 4 foot by 3 foot by 1 foot hole in the garden and bury a tomato.

10 Take up a paving stone outside the house. Ring the local council and say, 'It's a disgrace what I've just done.'

11 Make a Hollandaise sauce in 10 minutes and present it in a shoe.

12 Make a grass skirt and present an erotic hoola-hoop style dance.

13 Wet a towel and flick at people until a proper fight breaks out.

14 In five minutes search through all the TV channels and find someone called John.

15 Put lipstick on your cat or dog.

16 Sing three Boomtown Rats' songs from inside a wardrobe.

17 Dye yourself green by bathing in pea juice.

18 Collect six insects from the garden and place them on six heated spoons to see which one survives the longest.

19 Braid your hair using macaroni and Hula Hoops.

20 Stand on a street corner shouting 'Big Issue' for two minutes.

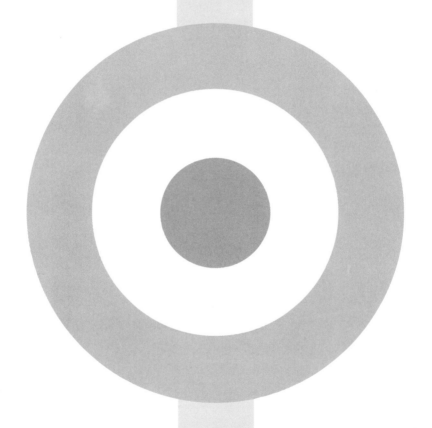

PRINTED IN BELGIUM BY
proost
INTERNATIONAL BOOK PRODUCTION